Revise IGCSE

Complete Study
&
Revision Guide

Mark Patmore
Brian Seager

Mathematics

FOUNDATION® BOOKS

Contents

 **Number**

 **Algebra**

3 Shape and Space

4 Handling Data

Aims, objectives and assessment

Aims

The aims of the CIE IGCSE course are clearly stated in the syllabus. These aims are the same for all students, and are statements of the long-term goals that the syllabus strives to achieve. You should be able to:

- develop knowledge and oral, written and practical skills to foster confidence and enjoyment, and be able to read, write and speak about mathematics clearly

- carry out calculations, solve and check problems, and understand the significance of results

- apply mathematics in everyday life, especially in science and technology, and understand the role that mathematics plays in the patterns and functioning of the world around them

- reason, classify, generalise and apply principles of logical poof with rigour, precision and logic

- have a sound preparation for further studies in mathematics.

Assessment objectives

These are the readily testable areas of mathematics, that will come up in examinations. You should be able to:

- present information neatly and accurately as diagrams, tables, graphs and written explanatory formats and make logical deductions from given data

- perform calculations by hand or by calculator, setting work out neatly

- understand measurement systems and estimation, working to appropriate degrees of accuracy

- use mathematical instruments to measure, construct and draw

- use mathematical knowledge in everyday situations and problems, selecting suitable methods of solution

- recognise patterns and structures and form generalisations in words or formula

- combine various skills to focus on problem solving.

Assessment

Assessment may be taken **with** or **without** coursework. Many schools in India choose the examination, and not the coursework, route.

In 2008, the non-coursework syllabus code is 0580.

You will sit either for:

- papers 1 (one hour, short answer questions, 35% of total marks) and 3 (two hours, structured questions, 65% of total marks), if you are doing the core curriculum,

  or:

- papers 2 (1½ hours, short-answer questions, 35% of total marks) and 4 (2½ hours, structured questions, 65% of total marks), if you are following the extended curriculum.

In all the papers, you must attempt all the questions; no choices are given. You are allowed a calculator for all papers.

If you follow the core curriculum, the highest grade you can obtain is C and the lowest is G.

If you follow the extended curriculum, the highest grade you can obtain is A* (A-star) and the lowest is E.

If the coursework option is followed (syllabus 0581), paper 1 of the core curriculum and paper 3 of the extended curriculum carry 30% of the total marks each and paper 2 of the core and paper 4 of the extended carry 50% each while coursework accounts for 20% of the total marks.

Preparing for the examination

Planning your study

The final three months before taking your IGCSE examination are very important in achieving your best grade. However, your success can be assisted by adopting an organised approach throughout the course.

- After completing a topic in school or college, go through the topic again in *Revise IGCSE Maths Study Guide*. Copy out the main points, results and formulae, etc. on a sheet of paper or use a highlighter pen to emphasise them.
- A few days later try to write out these key points again from memory. Check any differences between what you originally wrote and what you wrote later.
- If you have written your notes on a piece of paper keep this for revision to be done later.
- Try some questions in the book and check your answers.
- Decide whether you have fully mastered the topic and write down any weaknesses you think you have.

Preparing a revision programme

At least three months before the final examination, look at the list of topics in your awarding body's specification. Go through and identify which topics you feel you need to concentrate on. It is a temptation at this time to spend valuable revision time on the things you already know and can do. It makes you feel good but does not move you forward.

When you feel you have mastered all the topics, spend time trying past questions. Each time check your answers with the answers given. In the final couple of weeks go back to your summary sheets (or your highlighting in the book).

How this book will help you

Revise IGCSE Mathematics Guide will help you because:

- It contains the **essential content** for your IGCSE course without the extra material that will not be examined.
- It contains **progress checks** and **IGCSE questions** to help confirm your understanding.
- It gives **sample IGCSE questions** with **model answers** and advice from examiners on how to improve.
- The examination questions for 2003 are different from those in 2002 or 2001. Trying past questions will not help you when answering some parts of the questions in 2003. The questions in this book have been **written by experienced examiners** who are writing the questions for 2003 and beyond.
- The summary table and specification labels will give you a **quick reference** to the requirements for your examination.
- **Marginal comments** and highlighted **key points** will draw your attention to important things you might otherwise miss.

improve your grade

1 Read the instructions carefully

Some of the instructions could be:

- **Answer *ALL* the questions.**
  This means answer as many as you can. Only by getting all of them right will you obtain full marks.

- **Write your answers in the spaces provided on the question paper.**
  You are not allowed to use any other paper.

- In the exam you should **check** that you have been given the **correct paper**, that you know **how many questions** you have to answer on that paper and **how long** you have to do it. Try to spread your time equally between the questions. If you do this, it will avoid the desire to rush the paper or spend too much time on some questions and not finish the paper.

- Many mathematics papers start with fairly straightforward questions which may be shorter than those that follow. If this is the case, **work through them in order** to build up your confidence. Do not overlook any part of a question and **double check** that you have seen everything on each paper, look especially at the back page in case there is a question there!

- **Take time** to read through all the questions carefully and then start with the question(s) that you think you can do best.

- When there are about 15 minutes remaining in the examination then quickly check if you are running out of time. If you think that you will run out of time then try to score as many marks as possible by concentrating on the easier parts, the first parts, of any questions that you have not yet attempted.

2 Read the question carefully

- Make sure you **understand what the question is asking**. Some questions are **structured** and some are unstructured – called 'multi-step' questions – and for these you will have to decide how to tackle the question and it would be worthwhile spending a few seconds thinking the question through.

- Make sure you understand key words. The following glossary may help you in answering questions:

  Write down, state — no explanation is needed for an answer

  Calculate, find, show, solve — include enough working to make your method clear

  Draw — plot accurately using the graph paper provided and selecting a suitable scale if one is not given. Such an instruction is usually followed by asking you to read one or more values from your graph.

- The number of marks is given in brackets [ ] at the end of each question or part question. This gives some indication of **how many steps** will be required to answer the question and therefore what **proportion of your time** you should spend on each part of the question.

3 Show your working and check your answers

- **State units** if required and give your final answer to an **appropriate degree of accuracy**.
- Write down the figures on your calculator and then **make a suitable rounding**. Don't round the numbers during the calculation. This will often result in an incorrect answer.
- Don't forget to **check your answers**, especially to see that they are reasonable. The mean height of a group of men will not be 187 metres!
- **Lay out** your working **carefully** and **concisely**. Write down the calculations you are going to make. You usually get marks for showing a correct method. (If you are untidy and disorganised, you might misread some of your own work and/or lose marks because the examiner cannot read your work or follow your method.)
- **Remember** that marks are given for the following:
  - using an **appropriate method** to answer a question
  - for **facts found** as you work through a question
  - for the **final answer.**
- **Remember** that if all that is written down is an answer and that answer is wrong, you gain no marks. Once you have finished the paper, if you have any time left, **check the work** you have done. The best way to do this is to work through the questions again.

4 What examiners look for

The examiners look for the following:

- Work which is **legible, clearly set out** and **easy to follow** and understand. Use a pen, not pencil, except in drawings, and use the appropriate equipment.
- That drawings and graphs are **neat**, and **graphs are labelled**.
- That you always **indicate** how you **obtain your answers**.
- **The right answer!**

5 Practice makes perfect

- Practise all aspects of **manipulative algebra, solving equations, rearranging formulas, expanding brackets, factorising**, etc.
- Practise **answering questions** that ask for an **explanation**. Your answers should be **concise** and use **mathematical terms** where appropriate.
- Practise **answering questions** with **more than one step** to the answer, e.g. finding the radius of a sphere with the same volume as a given cone.
- Make sure you can use your **calculator efficiently**.

Unit 1 Number

Overview

Topic	Section	Studied in class	Revised	Practice questions
1.1 Integers	**Negative integers**			
	Ordering			
	Common factors and multiples			
	Prime numbers			
1.2 Powers and roots	**Square roots and cube roots**			
	Index laws			
	Inverse operations			
	Standard index form			
	More about standard form			
1.3 The four rules	**Equivalent fractions**			
	Addition of fractions			
	Multiplication and division			
1.4 Decimals	**Operations on decimals**			
	Decimals and fractions			
1.5 Percentages	**Percentages and fractions**			
	Percentages and decimals			
	One quantity as a percentages of another			
	Finding a percentage of a quantity			
	Finding a percentage increase or decrease			
	Reversed percentages			
1.6 Bank interest				
1.7 Ratio	**Simplifying ratios**			
	Dividing in a ratio			
1.8 Money				
1.9 Measures and time	**Measures**			
	Time			
1.10 Mental methods	**Recall**			
	Rounding numbers			
	Estimates			
	Limits of accuracy			
1.11 Written methods	**Proportional change**			
	Irrational numbers			
1.12 Calculator methods	**Understanding keys and display**			
	Upper and lower bounds			
	Exponential growth and decay			
1.13 Sets	**Defining a set**			
	Venn diagram			
	Subsets			
1.14 Solving problems	**Strategies**			
	Checking			

Number

1.1 Integers

After studying this section, you will be able to:

LEARNING SUMMARY

- use and understand negative integers
- use directed numbers in practical situations
- order quantities by magnitude
- find common factors and multiples
- recognise and use prime numbers

Negative integers

Integers are whole numbers, positive and negative.

They can be represented on a number line:

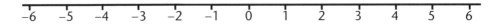

Moving (translating) to the right is adding, to the left subtracting.

A negative number is to the left of zero, a positive one to the right.

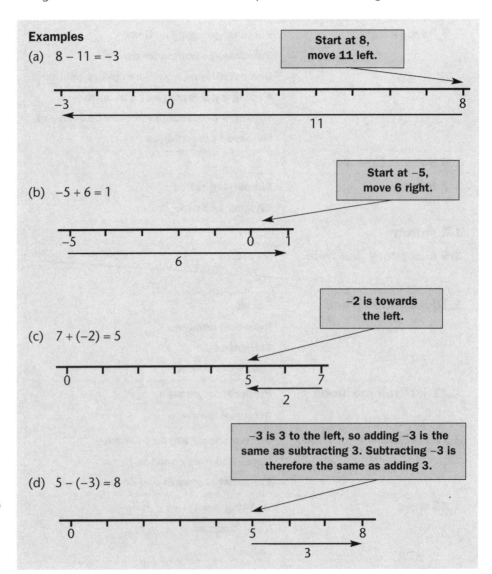

Examples

(a) $8 - 11 = -3$

Start at 8, move 11 left.

(b) $-5 + 6 = 1$

Start at −5, move 6 right.

(c) $7 + (-2) = 5$

−2 is towards the left.

−3 is 3 to the left, so adding −3 is the same as subtracting 3. Subtracting −3 is therefore the same as adding 3.

(d) $5 - (-3) = 8$

You will be expected to do calculations like these without a calculator.

Taking sea-level as zero, distance below the surface as negative and distances above the surface as positive, write down the integers corresponding to the following situations:

(a) A shark, swimming 30 m deep, sees a diver 10 m above him.

Position of Shark: _____   Position of Diver: _____

(b) The shark immediately rises 20 m to attack the diver, who dives deeper by 10 m.

Position of Shark: _____   Position of Diver: _____

(c) A rescue helicopter now comes to the diver's aid, and hovers 15 m above the surface.

Distance between helicopter and diver: _____

(d) The helicopter drops a shark repellent, which causes the shark to dive 25 m.

Position of Shark after diving: _____

(a) −30 m −20 m
(b) −10 m −30 m
(c) 45 m
(d) −35 m

Ordering

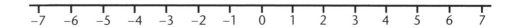

On this number line, the numbers on the right are greater than those on left.

So: **4** is greater than **1**,
      1 is greater than **−4**.

Similarly, **5** is less than **7**, but **−7** is less than **−5**
(because **−5** lies to the right of **−7**).

For 'less than', we use the symbol: <

For 'greater than', we use: >

So, looking at our number line, we can say:

$$-2 < 1 \text{ and } 4 > -3.$$

Sometimes, when we represent a quantity by a letter, say x, we can write down an inequality such as: $x < 3$, to show that we know that x is less than **3**.

If x is less than or equal to 3, we write $x \leqslant 3$.

Another way of expressing this is: x is *not greater than* **3**.

For example, x is not less than **−2** can be written as: $x \geqslant -2$

Of course, if x is equal to **3**, we simply write $x = 3$.

If x is not equal to **3**, we write $x \neq 3$.

Common factors and multiples

This section concerns positive integers.

 If you can divide one number by another, the second is a factor of the first.

For example, $12 \div 3 = 4$, so **3** is a factor of **12** (and so are **4**, **2**, **6**, **12** itself and, of course **1**).

 If you multiply one number by another, the result is a multiple of the first number (and also of the second number).

For example, **24** is a multiple of **6** (since $6 \times 4 = 24$). **24** is also a multiple of **2**, **3**, **4**, **8**, **12** and **24**.

Some numbers have **common** factors.

For example, **24** and **30** both have factors **2**, **3** and **6**.

The largest of these (6) is the **highest common factor (HCF)**.

Two (or more) numbers will have **common** multiples.

For example, **4** has multiples **4**, **8**, **12**, **16**, **20**, **24**, **28**, ...

3 has multiples **3**, **6**, **9**, **12**, **15**, **18**, **21**, **24**, **27**, ...

4 and **3** have common multiples **12**, **24**, ...

The smallest of these (12) is called the **lowest common multiple (LCM)**.

Prime numbers

A **prime Number** is a number that has only two distinct factors, or divisors — itself and unity,

So: **2** is a prime number, because it only has two factors — itself, (2) and unity (1).

Similarly, **3** is prime — its only factors are itself (3) and unity (1).

But, **4** is not prime – although **4** and **1** are factors, so is **2**.

Also, **1** is not prime – the number itself (1) and unity (1) are the same, and so not distinct.

To find all prime numbers up to fifty, we firstly list all the numbers as follows:

1	2	3	4	5	6	7	8	9	10
11	12	13	14	15	16	17	18	19	20
21	22	23	24	25	26	27	28	29	30
31	32	33	34	35	36	37	38	39	40
41	42	43	44	45	46	47	48	49	50

We now circle the first prime number, 2, and cross off all its multiples, as shown :

1	(2)	3	4̶	5	6̶	7	8̶	9	1̶0̶
11	1̶2̶	13	1̶4̶	1̶5̶	1̶6̶	17	1̶8̶	19	2̶0̶
21	2̶2̶	23	2̶4̶	25	2̶6̶	27	2̶8̶	29	3̶0̶
31	3̶2̶	33	3̶4̶	35	3̶6̶	37	3̶8̶	39	4̶0̶
41	4̶2̶	43	4̶4̶	4̶5̶	4̶6̶	47	4̶8̶	49	5̶0̶

When we have concluded the multiples of **2**, we then circle the next prime number and cross of all its multiples as follows:

1	(2)	(3)	4̶	5	6̶	7	8̶	9̶	1̶0̶
11	1̶2̶	13	1̶4̶	1̶5̶	1̶6̶	17	1̶8̶	19	2̶0̶
2̶1̶	2̶2̶	23	2̶4̶	25	2̶6̶	2̶7̶	2̶8̶	29	3̶0̶
31	3̶2̶	3̶3̶	3̶4̶	35	3̶6̶	37	3̶8̶	3̶9̶	4̶0̶
41	4̶2̶	43	4̶4̶	4̶5̶	4̶6̶	47	4̶8̶	49	5̶0̶

We then repeat the process for the next uncrossed number, **5**. This method, known as the Sieve of Aritosthenes, can be used to find all the prime numbers up to any limit.

The first prime numbers up to 50 are:

2, 3, 5, 7, 11, 13, 17, 19, 23, 29, 31, 37, 41, 43, 47.

When we want to write a number as a product of prime factors, we first divide by the lowest prime number, if possible, and continue to do so until not possible. We than more up to the next prime number, as shown.

If we want to write 504 as a product of primes, we notice that since 504 is even we can divide by 2 as follows:

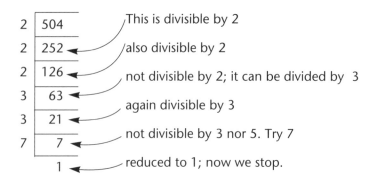

2	504	This is divisible by 2
2	252	also divisible by 2
2	126	not divisible by 2; it can be divided by 3
3	63	again divisible by 3
3	21	not divisible by 3 nor 5. Try 7
7	7	reduced to 1; now we stop.
	1	

So, reading the divisors downwards, we have:

$$504 = 2 \times 2 \times 2 \times 3 \times 3 \times 7,$$

or $$504 = 2^3 \times 3^2 \times 7^1$$

All positive integers can be written as a **product of prime factors**.

For example, $11 = (1 \times)11$

$12 = 2 \times 2 \times 3$

$39 = 3 \times 13$

> **KEY POINT** Some numbers have no factor other than 1 and themselves. These are prime numbers. For example, 2, 11, 29 are prime numbers.

Examples

(a) Write 24 and 75 as a product of prime factors.
Hence find the LCM and HCF of 24 and 75.

2	24
2	12
2	6
3	3
	1

$24 = 2 \times 2 \times 2 \times 3$

3	75
5	25
5	5
	1

$75 = 3 \times 5 \times 5$

LCM must include $2 \times 2 \times 2 \times 3$ and $3 \times 5 \times 5$ but the 3 is repeated.

So LCM $= 2 \times 2 \times 2 \times 3 \times 5 \times 5 = 600$

The only common factor is 3, so 3 is the HCF.

 You do not need a calculator to do these.

(b) Find the LCM and HCF of 56 and 84.

2	56
2	28
2	14
7	7
	1

$56 = 2 \times 2 \times 2 \times 7$

2	84
2	42
3	21
7	7
	1

$84 = 2 \times 2 \times 3 \times 7$

What do you notice about the repeated factors and the HCF?

LCM must include all factors but $2 \times 2 \times 7$ are repeated.

So LCM $= 2 \times 2 \times 2 \times 3 \times 7 = 168$

HCF $= 2 \times 2 \times 7 = 28$

With practice, you can do these in your head but it is sensible to write down each step, as here. In an exam, you will be expected to do this sort of calculation without a calculator.

PROGRESS CHECK

1 Work out:
  (a) $5 + (-6) - (-3)$ (b) $-8 + 7 - (-9)$ (c) $2 + (-11) + (-3)$
2 Find (i) the prime factors (ii) the LCM and (iii) the HCF of these numbers.
  (a) 27 and 36 (b) 75 and 60 (c) 18, 24 and 27.

1 (a) 2 (b) 8 (c) −12
2 (a)(i) 27 = 3 × 3 × 3; 36 = 2 × 2 × 3 × 3 (ii) 108 (iii) 9
  (b)(i) 75 = 3 × 5 × 5; 60 = 2 × 2 × 3 × 5 (ii) 300 (iii) 15
  (c)(i) 18 = 2 × 3 × 3; 24 = 2 × 2 × 2 × 3; 27 = 3 × 3 × 3 (ii) 216 (iii) 3

 **Number**

1.2 Powers and roots

LEARNING SUMMARY

After studying this section, you will be able to:

● **find square roots and cube roots**
● **understand index laws**
● **use inverse operations**
● **use standard index form**
● **make calculations using standard form**

Square roots and cube roots

 KEY POINT
A **square root** of a number must be squared (that is multiplied by itself or raised to the power 2) to give the number.

Any positive number has two square roots, one positive and one negative.

For example, the square roots of **49** are **7** and **−7**.

 KEY POINT
The **cube root** of a number must be cubed (that is raised to the power 3) to give the number.

You can use your calculator to find square roots but it will only give the positive ones. Use the $\boxed{x^y}$ key to find the cube root.

For example, the cube root of **64** is **4**.

These can be written

$$\sqrt{49}, \quad \sqrt[3]{64}$$

Index laws

Using an index is a shorthand way to show multiplication and division.

For example, $2 \times 2 \times 2 = 2^3$, $3 \times 3 \times 3 \times 3 \times 3 = 3^5$

Examples

Do not confuse 2^3 (= 8) with 2×3 (= 6)!

(a)   Use indices to find 16×32.

$16 = 2 \times 2 \times 2 \times 2 \; (= 2^4)$, $32 = 2 \times 2 \times 2 \times 2 \times 2 \; (= 2^5)$,

$16 \times 32 = 2 \times 2 \times 2 \times 2 \times 2 \times 2 \times 2 \times 2 \times 2 \; (= 2^9)$

You can see that $2^4 \times 2^5 = 2^9$.

 KEY POINT
This is an example of the **index law for multiplication**:
$a^p \times a^q = a^{p+q}$

(b) Use indices to find $81 \div 9$.

$81 = 3 \times 3 \times 3 \times 3 \ (= 3^4)$, $9 = 3 \times 3 \ (= 3^2)$

$$81 \div 9 = \frac{81}{9} = \frac{3 \times 3 \times 3 \times 3}{3 \times 3} = 3 \times 3$$

This time $3^4 \div 3^2 = 3^{4-2} = 3^2$.

> **KEY POINT**
> This uses the **index law for division**:
> $$a^p \div a^q = a^{p-q}$$

(c) Find $(2^3)^4$.

This is

Don't add the indices this time!

$$(2^3) \times (2^3) \times (2^3) \times (2^3) = 2 \times 2 \times 2 \times 2 \times 2 \times 2 \times 2 \times 2 \times 2 \times 2 \times 2 \times 2$$
$$= 2^{12} = 2^{3 \times 4}$$

> **KEY POINT**
> This shows another index law:
> $$\left(a^p\right)^q = a^{p \times q}$$

(d) Simplify $\dfrac{2^3 \times (3^2)^4}{2^2 \times 3^5}$.

This equals

You can cancel the factors that are common to the top and bottom of the fraction, using the index law for division.

$$\frac{2^3 \times 3^8}{2^2 \times 3^5} = \frac{2^3}{2^2} \times \frac{3^8}{3^5} = 2 \times 3^3$$

(e) Use the index law for division to find $\dfrac{2^3}{2^3}$.

$$\frac{2^3}{2^3} = 2^{3-3} = 2^0$$

But $\dfrac{2^3}{2^3} = 1$, so $2^0 = 1$.

> **KEY POINT**
> This demonstrates another index law:
> $$a^0 = 1$$

(f) Use the index law for division to find $\dfrac{1}{3^2}$.

$\dfrac{1}{a}$ **is the reciprocal of *a*.**

$$\frac{1}{3^2} = \frac{3^0}{3^2} = 3^{0-2} = 3^{-2}$$

> **KEY POINT**
> This is an example of the index law:
> $$\frac{1}{a^p} = a^{-p}$$

(g) If $\sqrt{2} = 2^x$, find the value of x.

$$\left(\sqrt{2}\right)^2 = \left(2^x\right)^2$$

$2 = 2^{2x}$, giving $2x = 1$ and $x = \frac{1}{2}$.

> **Square both sides:**
> $$\left(\sqrt{2}\right)^2 = 2 = 2^1$$

> **KEY POINT**
> The general law is:
> $$\sqrt[n]{a} = a^{\frac{1}{n}}$$

Inverse operations

> **KEY POINT**
> The operation which reverses what has been done is called an **inverse operation.**

For example, The inverse of **adding 7** is **subtracting 7**;

the inverse of **dividing by 10** is **multiplying by 10**;

the inverse of **taking a reciprocal** is **taking the reciprocal again**;

Remember that
$$\sqrt[n]{a} = a^{\frac{1}{n}}.$$

the inverse of $\sqrt[n]{a}$ is $\left(\sqrt[n]{a}\right)^n$, which equals a.

> $$\frac{1}{\frac{1}{a}} = a \text{ (Multiply top and bottom by } a.)$$

Standard index form

There is a special form of index notation, which is very useful for showing large and small numbers.

For example,

$14\,000\,000 = 1.4 \times 10\,000\,000 = 1.4 \times 10 \times 10 \times 10 \times 10 \times 10 \times 10 \times 10$
$$= 1.4 \times 10^7$$

> **KEY POINT**
> This is called standard index form. The number is expressed as a number between 1 and 10 multiplied by 10 to the appropriate index.

Find out how your calculator uses standard index form — how to enter numbers and how to read them. For example, your calculator may display 4.96^{05}, which you must write as 4.96×10^5. When keying numbers in, you do not usually have to enter the 10. (See Section 1.12)

Examples

(a) Write 2.7×10^4 as an ordinary number.

$$2.7 \times 10^4 = 2.7 \times 10 \times 10 \times 10 \times 10 = 27\,000$$

(b) Write 4.96×10^{-5} as an ordinary number.

$$4.96 \times 10^{-5} = 4.96 \div 10^5 = 0.000\,0496$$

Any of the three answers in this example is correct — unless the question asked for the answer in standard index form, when only 1.2×10^3 is right.

(c) Work out without using a calculator:

$$3 \times 10^6 \times 4 \times 10^{-4}$$
$$3 \times 10^6 \times 4 \times 10^{-4} = 3 \times 4 \times 10^{6-4} = 12 \times 10^2 = 1200 = 1.2 \times 10^3$$

(d) Work out, without using a calculator:

$$4.7 \times 10^4 + 8.2 \times 10^5$$
$$4.7 \times 10^4 + 8.2 \times 10^5 = 47\,000 + 820\,000 = 867\,000 = 8.67 \times 10^5$$

Unless you are asked to write down all the figures in your display (8.78561872 in this case), give your answer to sensible accuracy. See Section 1.10.

(e) Use a calculator to find:

$$\frac{7.23 \times 10^5 \times 1.09 \times 10^{-3}}{8.97 \times 10^{-4}}$$

You should find the answer is 8.79×10^5, correct to two d.p.

More about standard form

In science and technology, we often deal with numbers that are either very small or very large. Look at these numbers:

$$300,000,000 \text{ ms}^{-1}; \quad 0.000000590 \text{ m}.$$

The first number is difficult to read. It is much easier to deal with, if we write it as a number with a power of ten:

You may note that this is actually the speed of light in a vacuum.

$$300,000,000 \text{ ms}^{-1} = 3.0 \times 10^8 \text{ ms}^{-1}$$

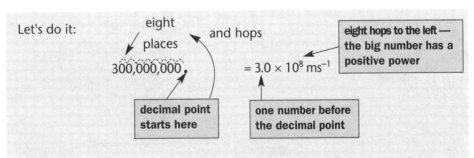

Here are some more examples of large numbers being written in standard form:

$$19,508,325 = 1.9508325 \times 10^7$$
$$234,000,000,000 = 2.34 \times 10^{11}$$

For a small number:

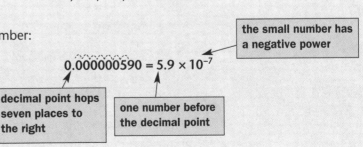

Here are some examples of small numbers, written in standard form:

$$0.0000009102 = 9.102 \times 10^{-7}$$
$$0.000564 = 5.64 \times 10^{-4}$$

When we multiply numbers in standard from, such as: $(3.1 \times 10^{11}) \times (6.0 \times 10^{-7})$ we:

(a) multiply the numbers together: $3.1 \times 6.0 = 18.6$

(b) add the indices together: $10^{11} \times 10^{-7} = 10^4$

(c) write the number as a whole, adjusting it so that there is one number before the decimal point.

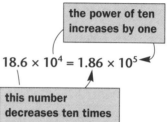

the power of ten increases by one

$$18.6 \times 10^4 = 1.86 \times 10^5$$

this number decreases ten times

Examples

$$5.82 \times 10^9 \times 3.6 \times 10^8 = 20.952 \times 10^{17}$$
$$= 2.0952 \times 10^{18}$$
$$(6.4 \times 10^{-5}) \times (4.2 \times 10^{-3}) = 26.88 \times 10^{-8}$$
$$= 2.688 \times 10^{-7}$$

Note that −7 is bigger than −8.

When we **divide** numbers in standard form

(a) we divide the numbers

(b) subtract the indices

(c) adjust so that there is one number before the decimal point.

$$(1.96 \times 10^8) \div (6.4 \times 10^4) = 0.30625 \times 10^{8-4}$$
$$= 0.30625 \times 10^4 = 3.0625 \times 10^3$$

this number _increases_ by a factor of ten, so the index _decreases_ from 4 to 3, i.e. by a power of 10.

Examples

$$(2.85 \times 10^{-7}) \div (1.3 \times 10^{-9})$$
$$= 2.19 \times 10^{-7-(-9)} = 2.19 \times 10^2$$

to 3 significant figures

$$(5.64 \times 10^{-8}) \div (8.2 \times 10^4) = 0.688 \times 10^{-12} = 6.88 \times 10^{-13}$$

to 3 significant figures   **ten times bigger**

When we add or subtract numbers, first we should make the indices the same and then:

• in the case of addition, we add the numbers and keep the same index

• in the case of subtraction, we subtract the numbers and keep the same index.

Examples

Add: $(5.08 \times 10^9) + (7.34 \times 10^{10})$

Changing the first number so that the index of both the numbers is 10:

$$(0.508 \times 10^{10}) + (7.34 \times 10^{10})$$

Now we add the numbers while the index remains unchanged:

$$7.848 \times 10^{10}$$

Subtract: $(6.23 \times 10^{-8}) - (4.72 \times 10^{-7})$

Noting that -7 is greater them -8, we change the first number to give:

$$(0.623 \times 10^{-7}) - (4.72 \times 10^{-7}) = -4.097 \times 10^{-7}.$$

You should check that:
(a) $(5.8 \times 10^6) \times (6.4 \times 10^{-4}) = 37.12 \times 10^2 = 3.712 \times 10^3$
(b) $(5.8 \times 10^6) \div (6.4 \times 10^{-4}) = 0.906 \times 10^{10} = 9.06 \times 10^9$
(c) $(5.8 \times 10^6) + (6.4 \times 10^4) = 5.864 \times 10^6$
(d) $(5.8 \times 10^6) - (6.4 \times 10^5) = 5.16 \times 10^6$

The Earth is 150 million kilometres away from the Sun while Venus is only 80 million kilometres from the Sun.
(a) Write both the distances in standard form.
(b) Calculate the distance between the Earth and Venus, when they form a straight line with the sun but are:
   (i) on the same side of the sun (diagram 1)
   (ii) on opposite sides of the sun (diagram 2).
(c) Calculate the direct distance between the Earth and Venus when they form a right angle with the Sun (diagram 3).

Answers:
(a) 1.5×10^8 km; 8.0×10^7 km.

(b)

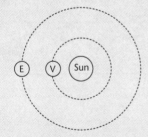   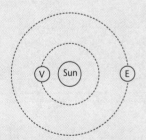

Earth/Venus distance

$= (1.5 \times 10^8) - (8.0 \times 10^7)$ km
$= (1.5 \times 10^8) - (0.8 \times 10^8)$ km
$= 0.7 \times 10^8$ km
$= 7.0 \times 10^7$ km.

Earth/Venus distance

$= (1.5 \times 10^8) + (8.0 \times 10^7)$ km
$= (1.5 \times 10^8) + (0.8 \times 10^8)$ km
$= 2.3 \times 10^8$ km

(c)

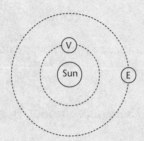

Now Venus–Sun–Earth form a right-angled triangle with one side of length 15 units and another of length 8 units. So Venus–Earth distance is,

$= \sqrt{8^2 + 15^2}$ (by Pythagoras theorem)

$= 17$ units

$= 170$ million kms.

Without using a calculator

1 Write as ordinary numbers:

(a) $\sqrt[3]{125}$ (b) 3^4 (c) $\sqrt{196}$ (d) 3.2×10^5 (e) $4^{-\frac{1}{2}}$

2 Simplify, leaving your answer in index form:

(a) $5^4 \times 5^3$ (b) $7^3 \div 7^5$ (c) $(3^2)^5$ (d) $\sqrt[3]{5}$ (e) $\dfrac{1}{13^4}$

3 Write in standard index form, as simply as possible:

(a) 0.021 (b) 48 700 (c) $\dfrac{1}{4}$ (d) 1.008 (e) $5 \times 10^3 \times 2 \times 10^6$

(f) $8 \times 10^2 \div (4 \times 10^3)$

PROGRESS CHECK

Using a calculator

4 Work out the following, leaving your answers in standard index form:

(a) $3.7 \times 10^6 \times 1.02 \times 10^2$ (b) $4.5633 \times 10^8 \div (3.71 \times 10^2)$

(c) $1.57 \times 10^{-2} \times 3.81 \times 10^4$ (d) $7.81 \times 10^{-4} \div (9.734 \times 10^6)$

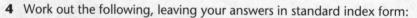

4 (a) 3.774×10^8 (b) 1.23×10^6 (c) 5.9817×10^2 (d) 8.023×10^{-11}

3 (a) 2.1×10^{-2} (b) 4.87×10^4 (c) 2.5×10^{-1} (d) 1.008 (e) 1.0×10^{10} (f) 2.0×10^{-1}

2 (a) 5^7 (b) 7^{-2} (c) 3^{10} (d) $5^{\frac{1}{3}}$ (e) 13^{-4}

1 (a) 5 (b) 81 (c) 14 (d) 320 000 (e) $\dfrac{1}{2}$ or 0.5

1.3 The four rules

After studying this section, you will be able to:

LEARNING SUMMARY

- ● **find and use equivalent fractions**
- ● **add and subtract fractions**
- ● **multiply and divide fractions**
- ● **use the four rules for calculations involving fractions**
- ● **understand the correct ordering of arithmetic operations**

Equivalent fractions

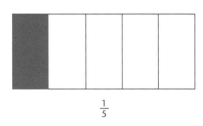

$\frac{1}{5}$

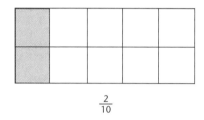

$\frac{2}{10}$

KEY POINT

If you multiply (or divide) the top (numerator) and the bottom (denominator) of a fraction by the same number, the value of the two fractions is the same. These are called **equivalent fractions.**

For example, $\frac{1}{5} = \frac{1 \times 2}{5 \times 2} = \frac{2}{10}$ and $\frac{18}{72} = \frac{18 \div 9}{72 \div 9} = \frac{2}{8} = \frac{2 \div 2}{8 \div 2} = \frac{1}{4}$

Using this, fractions can be put in order, simplified, added and subtracted.

Examples

(a) Write these fractions in order, smallest first.

$$\frac{2}{3}, \frac{3}{5}, \frac{4}{7}, \frac{13}{20}$$

> Find the LCM.
> 5 is a factor of 20.

The common denominator must have factors 3, 5, 7, 20.

LCM = 3 × 5 × 7 × 4 = 420

If a calculator is allowed, then this is done more quickly by turning the fractions into decimals. On a non-calculator paper you must use this method.

$$\frac{2}{3} = \frac{2 \times 5 \times 7 \times 4}{3 \times 5 \times 7 \times 4} = \frac{280}{420}, \quad \frac{3}{5} = \frac{3 \times 3 \times 7 \times 4}{5 \times 3 \times 7 \times 4} = \frac{252}{420}$$

$$\frac{4}{7} = \frac{4 \times 3 \times 5 \times 4}{7 \times 3 \times 5 \times 4} = \frac{240}{420} \quad \frac{13}{20} = \frac{13 \times 3 \times 7}{20 \times 3 \times 7} = \frac{273}{420}$$

> Make sure you multiply the numerator and denominator by the same numbers in each case.

So the order is $\frac{4}{7}, \frac{3}{5}, \frac{13}{20}, \frac{2}{3}$

(b) Write as simply as possible: $\frac{160}{280}$

> This process is called cancelling.

$$\frac{160}{280} = \frac{160 \div 10}{280 \div 10} = \frac{16}{28} = \frac{16 \div 4}{28 \div 4} = \frac{4}{7}$$

Now we look at the four rules of: addition, subtraction, multiplication, division applied to fractions and decimals.

Addition of fractions

$$\boxed{\text{numerator}} \longrightarrow \quad \boxed{\text{denominator}} \longrightarrow \quad \frac{3}{4} + \frac{2}{3}$$

Note that multiplying numbers always yields a common multiple, but not necessarily the lowest one (here 12 is the lowest common multiple i.e. LCM of 4 and 3).

First, the denominators (the numbers on the bottom of the fractions) need to be the same. We must find a **common multiple**.

A common multiple of **4** and **3** can be found by multiplying them: **4 × 3 = 12**.

For example, for **4** and **6**, the LCM is not **24**, but **12**, because both **4** and **6** contain the factor **2**.

> **Example**
> The LCM of 5 and 10 is 10; the LCM of 12 and 16 is 48.

To proceed:

> We multiply the numerator by 3 since we have multiplied the denominator (4) by 3

Twelve-twelfths make one whole unit and there will be five twelfths left over.

$$\frac{3}{4} + \frac{2}{3} = \frac{9+8}{12} = \frac{17}{12}, \text{ and } \frac{17}{12} \text{ can be written as } 1\frac{5}{12}.$$

> For second fraction, we multiply both numerator and denominator by 4.

If whole numbers are involved, we add the whole numbers together and the fractions together and then adjust the result:

$$2\frac{4}{9} + 3\frac{7}{12} = 5\frac{16+21}{36}$$

$$5\frac{37}{36} = 6\frac{1}{36}$$

36 is the LCM of 9 and 12.

> We use 36 of these 37 to make a whole unit.

Similarly, for subtraction:

$$8\frac{5}{6} - 2\frac{3}{4} = 6\frac{10-9}{12} = 6\frac{1}{12}.$$

LCM

We may have to borrow a unit:

> Here, we would get a negative number, so we take a whole unit from 6, and convert it into thirtieths

$$9\frac{2}{5} - 3\frac{5}{6} = 6\frac{12-25}{30}$$

> This has been reduced by 1 unit

$$= 5\frac{30+12-25}{30} = 5\frac{17}{30}$$

Example

$$7\frac{4}{9} - 2\frac{11}{12} = 5\frac{16-33}{36}$$

$$= 4\frac{36+16-33}{36} = 4\frac{19}{36}$$

Putting addition and subtraction together:

$$5\frac{3}{8} + 2\frac{4}{5} - 3\frac{7}{10} = 4\frac{15+32-28}{40} = 4\frac{19}{40}.$$

Multiplication and division

Before proceeding, we will learn to convert mixed numbers into improper fractions.

Step 1: See if you can cancel above and below the line to make the work simpler.

Step 2: Multiply numerators together; multiply denominators together. Adjust your answer back to a mixed number, if necessary.

Example

Each whole unit consists of three thirds, so **2 = six thirds**. Hence $2\frac{2}{3}$ = eight-thirds

$$2\frac{2}{3} \times 1\frac{4}{5} = \frac{8}{3} \times \frac{9}{5}$$

Now, $\frac{8}{{}_1\cancel{3}} \times \frac{\cancel{9}^3}{5}$ on cancellation gives $= \frac{24}{5} = 4\frac{4}{5}$ (on adjusting).

$$3\frac{4}{7} \times 4\frac{2}{3} = \frac{25}{{}_1\cancel{7}} \times \frac{\cancel{14}^2}{3} = \frac{50}{3} = 16\frac{2}{3}$$

For division, first understand that division by a number gives the same answer as multiplying by its reciprocal;

$$1 \div 2 = \frac{1}{2}, \text{ and } 1 \times \frac{1}{2} = \frac{1}{2}.$$

We have the same result, as the reciprocal of **2** is **1/2** (by 'reciprocal' we simply mean the number turned upside down, or inverted).

The reciprocal of 4 $\left(\text{or } \frac{4}{1}\right)$ is $\frac{1}{4}$.

The reciprocal of $\frac{2}{3}$ is $\frac{3}{2}$.

The reciprocal of $1\frac{3}{5}\left(\text{or }\frac{8}{5}\right)$, is $\frac{5}{8}$.

> **KEY POINT**   When dividing by a fraction, we multiply by its reciprocal.

$\frac{4}{3} \div \frac{2}{9}$ can be rewritten as $\frac{\cancel{4}^2}{{}_1\cancel{3}} \times \frac{\cancel{9}^3}{{}_1\cancel{2}} = \frac{6}{1} = 6$.

Similarly, $1\frac{3}{5} \div \frac{4}{7} = \frac{8}{5} \times \frac{7}{\cancel{4}_1}^2 = \frac{14}{5} = 2\frac{4}{5}$.

Before looking at decimals, let us look at the order in which the operations concerning the four rules are carried out:

ORDER
OF
OPERATION

B rackets

o f

D ivision

M ultiplication

A ddition

S ubtraction

Examples

(a) $$5(3 + 4) - 14 \div (9 - 2)$$

First of all, we carry out the operations in the brackets to give

$$5(7) - 14 \div (7).$$

Then remove the brackets by multiplying and dividing:

$$35 - 2.$$

Finally, do the subtraction to give the solution 33.

(b) $$6 + 4(7 - 2) - 5 (4 \div 2)$$
$$= 6 + 4(5) - 5(2) = 6 + 20 - 10 = 16$$

(c) Applying the rules to fractions

$$1\frac{3}{4}\left(3\frac{1}{5} - 2\frac{2}{3}\right) \div \frac{3}{4}$$

$$1\frac{3}{4}\left(1\frac{3 - 10}{15}\right) \div \frac{3}{4}$$

$$= \frac{7}{4}\left(\frac{15 + 3 - 10}{15}\right) \times \frac{4}{3}$$

$$= \frac{7}{\underset{1}{4}}\left(\frac{8}{15}\right) \times \frac{\overset{1}{4}}{3} = \frac{56}{45} = 1\frac{11}{45}$$

1.4 Decimals

LEARNING SUMMARY

After studying this section, you will be able to:

- *perform four arithmetic operations on decimals*
- *change a fraction into a decimal*
- *change a decimal into a fraction*

Operations on decimals

KEY POINT

While adding or subtracting decimals, write the numbers under each other so that the decimal points are in a vertical line and then carry out the operation.

Examples (Addition and subtraction)

(a) $4.56 + 3.009 + 11.1$

Writing these in columnar form:

$$\begin{array}{r} 4.56 \\ 3.009 \\ +11.1 \\ \hline 18.669 \end{array}$$

(b) $2.082 - 0.5026$

Writing these in columnar form:

$$\begin{array}{r} 2.0820 \\ -0.5026 \\ \hline 1.5794 \end{array}$$

| There was no number here, so we add a zero |

Examples (Multiplication)

(a) Multiply 3.2 with 5.1.

Write in columnar form with decimal points vertically aligned:

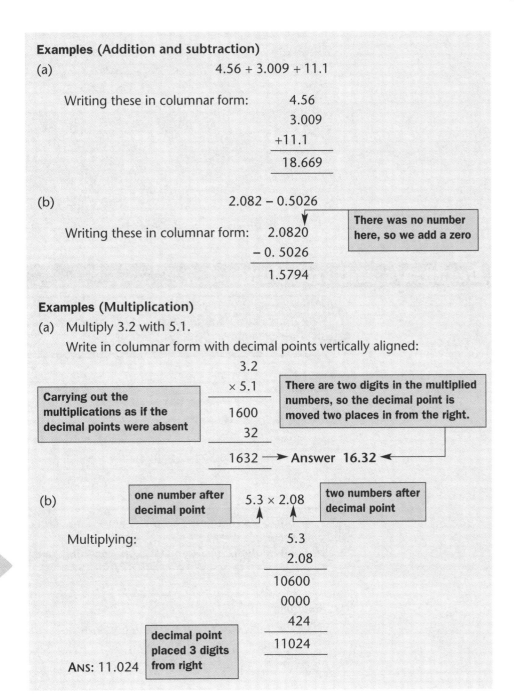

| Carrying out the multiplications as if the decimal points were absent |

$$\begin{array}{r} 3.2 \\ \times 5.1 \\ \hline 1600 \\ 32 \\ \hline 1632 \end{array}$$

| There are two digits in the multiplied numbers, so the decimal point is moved two places in from the right. |

$1632 \longrightarrow$ **Answer 16.32**

(b)

| one number after decimal point | 5.3×2.08 | two numbers after decimal point |

Multiplying:

| 3 digits in total after the decimal points |

$$\begin{array}{r} 5.3 \\ 2.08 \\ \hline 10600 \\ 0000 \\ 424 \\ \hline 11024 \end{array}$$

| decimal point placed 3 digits from right |

ANS: 11.024

If we are asked to carry out the division **8.032 ÷ 2.4**, we set out the question by moving the decimal point in the divisor (**2.4**) to the end of the number – in this case one place to the right to yield 24.

But the quotient (the number to be divided) should also have its decimal point adjusted by one place to the right. Hence, **8.032** becomes **80.32**.

So the question translates from: **8.032 ÷ 2.4**, to **80.32 ÷ 24** (in effect, both division and quotient have been multiplied by ten. Now we can divide:

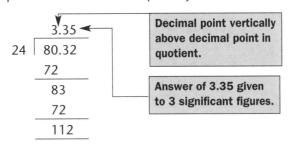

$$24 \overline{\smash{\big)}\ 80.32} \quad \to \quad 3.35$$

$$\begin{array}{r} 3.35 \\ 24\ \overline{\smash{)}\ 80.32} \\ 72 \\ \hline 83 \\ 72 \\ \hline 112 \end{array}$$

| Decimal point vertically above decimal point in quotient. |

| Answer of 3.35 given to 3 significant figures. |

Example

$$5.216 \div 2.74$$

We rewrite as: $521.6 \div 274$

and divide:

$$274 \overline{\smash{\big)}\ 521.600} \quad \underset{\text{1.903}}{}$$

> **Extra zeros to aid calculation up to 3 significant figures.**

$$\begin{array}{r} 274 \\ \hline 2476 \\ 2466 \\ \hline 1000 \end{array}$$

ANS: 1.90 (to 3 significant figures)

Decimals and fractions

> **KEY POINT**
> To change a fraction into a decimal, divide the numerator by the denominator.

Examples

(a) $\dfrac{2}{5} = 2 \div 5 = 0.4$

(b) $\dfrac{4}{7} = 4 \div 7 = 0.571\ 428\ 571\ \ldots$

> **The second decimal never stops. Can you see the repeating pattern?**

> **KEY POINT**
> Decimals that never stop and have a repeating pattern are called recurring decimals.
> All fractions give terminating or recurring decimals.

Example

Find decimals equivalent to these fractions:

$$\dfrac{13}{20}, \ \dfrac{2}{9}, \ \dfrac{5}{16}, \ \dfrac{5}{11}$$

$$\dfrac{13}{20} = 13 \div 20 = 0.65$$

$$\dfrac{2}{9} = 0.222\ 222\ 222\ \ldots$$

$$\dfrac{5}{16} = 0.3125$$

$$\dfrac{5}{11} = 0.454\ 545\ 454\ \ldots$$

> **Which fractions give terminating decimals?**

There is a simpler notation to show recurring decimals, using a dot above the number or numbers that make the pattern.

For example, $\dfrac{2}{9} = 0.222\ 222\ 222\ldots = 0.\dot{2}$

$$\dfrac{5}{11} = 0.454\ 545\ 45\ldots = 0.\dot{4}\dot{5}$$

> **In this case, put a dot over the first and last figures in the pattern.**

$$\dfrac{4}{7} = 0.571428\ 571\ldots = 0.\dot{5}7142\dot{8}$$

Example

Find fractions equivalent to these decimals:

$0.7, 0.125, 0.04, 0.034, 0.\dot{3}, 0.\dot{2}\dot{7}, 0.0\dot{6}$

$0.7 = \dfrac{7}{10}$

$0.125 = \dfrac{125}{1000} = \dfrac{5 \times 5 \times 5}{10 \times 10 \times 10} = \dfrac{1}{8}$

> Cancel by 5 and by 5 and by 5.

$0.04 = \dfrac{4}{100} = \dfrac{1}{25}$

$0.034 = \dfrac{34}{1000} = \dfrac{17}{500}$

$0.\dot{3}$ needs a different approach.

$$10 \times 0.\dot{3} = 3.333\,333\,33 \ldots$$
$$0.\dot{3} = 0.333\,333\,33 \ldots$$
$$\overline{10 \times 0.\dot{3} - 0.\dot{3} = 3}$$

> The two recurring parts are the same, so subtracting them gives 0.

$$9 \times 0.\dot{3} = 3, \text{ so } 0.\dot{3} = \dfrac{3}{9} = \dfrac{1}{3}$$

$$100 \times 0.\dot{2}\dot{7} = 27.272\,727\,27 \ldots$$
$$0.\dot{2}\dot{7} = 0.272\,727\,27 \ldots$$
$$\overline{100 \times 0.\dot{2}\dot{7} - 0.\dot{2}\dot{7} = 27}$$
$$99 \times 0.\dot{2}\dot{7} = 27$$
$$0.\dot{2}\dot{7} = \dfrac{27}{99} = \dfrac{3}{11}$$

> This is the same method as before with 100 instead of 10 as there are two numbers in the pattern.

$$\overline{10 \times 0.0\dot{6} = 0.666\,6 \ldots}$$
$$0.0\dot{6} = 0.066\,66 \ldots$$
$$9 \times 0.0\dot{6} = 0.6$$
$$0.0\dot{6} = \dfrac{0.6}{9} = \dfrac{6}{90} = \dfrac{1}{15}$$

Alternative method

$0.0\dot{6} = 0.\dot{6} \div 10 = \dfrac{2}{3} \div 10 = \dfrac{2}{30} = \dfrac{1}{15}$

---

1 Write as decimals:

   (a) $\dfrac{4}{5}$ (b) $\dfrac{13}{40}$ (c) $\dfrac{2}{3}$ (d) $\dfrac{5}{9}$ (e) $\dfrac{17}{33}$

2 Write as fractions in their lowest terms:

   (a) 0.15 (b) 0.046 (c) $0.\dot{7}$ (d) $0.\dot{3}$ (e) $0.\dot{5}\dot{4}$

PROGRESS CHECK

2 (a) $\dfrac{3}{20}$ (b) $\dfrac{23}{500}$ (c) $\dfrac{7}{9}$ (d) $\dfrac{1}{3}$ (e) $\dfrac{6}{11}$

1 (a) 0.8 (b) 0.325 (c) $0.\dot{6}$ (d) $0.\dot{5}$ (e) $0.\dot{5}\dot{1}$

1.5 Percentages

LEARNING SUMMARY

After studying this section, you will be able to:
- change percentages to fractions and vice versa
- change percentages to decimals and vice versa
- express one quantity as a percentage of another
- find a percentage of a quantity
- find a percentage increase or decrease
- use reversed percentages

Percentages and fractions

A percentage is a fraction with denominator **100**. **51%** means $\frac{51}{100}$.

KEY POINT To change a percentage to a fraction, write it over 100 and cancel any common factors.

Example

Write as fractions:

20%, 45%, 66%, 140%.

$200\% = \dfrac{20}{100} = \dfrac{1}{5}$ **Cancelling by 20**

$45\% = \dfrac{45}{100} = \dfrac{9}{20}$ **Cancelling by 5**

$66\% = \dfrac{66}{100} = \dfrac{33}{50}$ **Cancelling by 2**

 Beware! This is NOT, $\frac{2}{3}$, which is $66\frac{2}{3}\%$

The result is larger than 1 as the percentage is larger than 100.

$140\% = \dfrac{140}{100} = \dfrac{7}{5} = 1\dfrac{2}{5}$

KEY POINT To change a fraction to a percentage, multiply by 100%.

Example

Change to percentages:

$\dfrac{2}{5}, \dfrac{5}{8}, 1\dfrac{1}{2}, \dfrac{1}{3}$

 A percentage is the numerator of a fraction with 100 as denominator, so it is 100 times bigger than the fraction.

$\dfrac{2}{5} \times 100\% = \dfrac{2 \times 100}{5}\% = 2 \times 20\% = 40\%$

$\dfrac{5}{8} \times 100\% = \dfrac{5 \times 100}{8}\% = \dfrac{5 \times 25}{2}\% = 62\dfrac{1}{2}\%$

$$1\frac{1}{2} \times 100\% = 150\%$$

$$\frac{1}{3} \times 100\% = \frac{100}{3} = 33\frac{1}{3}\%$$

Or you could write $33.\dot{3}\%$

Don't make the common mistake of confusing 30% with $\frac{1}{3}$.

Percentages and decimals

 KEY POINT To change a percentage to a decimal, write it over 100 and divide it out.

Example

Write as decimals:

17.5%, 84%, 250%, 0.2%

$$\frac{17.5}{100} = 0.175, \quad \frac{84}{100} = 0.84, \quad \frac{250}{100} = 2.5, \quad \frac{0.2}{100} = 0.002$$

 KEY POINT To change a decimal to a percentage, multiply by 100%.

Examples

Write as percentages:

0.75, 0.29, 5.3, 0.0005.

$0.75 = 0.75 \times 100\% = 75\%,$ $0.29 = 0.29 \times 100\% = 29\%,$

$5.3 = 5.3 \times 100\% = 530\%,$ $0.0005 = 0.0005 \times 100\% = 0.05\%$

One quantity as a percentage of another

 KEY POINT To find one quantity as a percentage of another, divide the first by the second and multiply by 100%.

Examples

(a) What is 45 as a percentage of 150?

Cancel before multiplying if not using a calculator.

$$\text{Percentage} = \frac{45}{150} \times 100\% = \frac{3}{10} \times 100\% = 30\%$$

(b) Find 83 as a percentage of 745.

Round the answer to 3 significant figures.

$$\text{Percentage} = \frac{83}{745} \times 100\% = 11.14...\% = 11.1\%$$

Finding a percentage of a quantity

KEY POINT

To find the percentage of a quantity, multiply by the percentage and divide by 100.

> **Cancel before multiplying if not using a calculator.**

Examples

(a) Find 35% of 250.

$$\frac{35}{100} \times 250 = \frac{7}{20} \times 250 = \frac{7}{2} \times 25 = 87.5$$

(b) What is 6.5% of £23 500?

$$\frac{6.5}{100} \times 23\,500 = £1527.50$$

Finding a percentage increase or decrease

If a quantity is increased by a percentage, then that percentage of the quantity is added to the original.

For example,

if **$50** is increased by **15%**, the result is $\$50 + \$\frac{15}{100} \times 50 = \$57.50$

> **This is much quicker than adding the increase.**

This is the same as multiplying **50** by $1 + \frac{15}{100}$ or **1.15**.

KEY POINT

To find the result of a percentage increase, multiply by (1 + the percentage divided by 100).

> **To find a percentage increase, multiply by a number greater than 1.**

Examples

(a) Increase 42 by 23%.

To increase by 23%, multiply by 1.23

$$42 \times 1.23 = 51.66$$

$$1 + \frac{23}{100} = 1.23$$

(b) The price of cars increased by 2.5%.

What is the price of a car previously costing $10 500?

To increase by 2.5%, multiply by = 1.025

$$10\,500 \times 1.025 = \$10\,762.50$$

$$1 + \frac{2.5}{100} = 1.025$$

Finding a decrease works in the same way. This time the percentage is subtracted.

For example, if **$50** is decreased by **15%**, the result is $\$50 - \$\dfrac{15}{100} \times 50$

$= \$42.50$

This is the same as multiplying 50 by $1 - \dfrac{15}{100}$ or 0.85.

> **KEY POINT**
> To find the result of a percentage decrease, multiply by (**1** − **the percentage divided by 100**).

To find a percentage decrease, multiply by a number smaller than 1.

Examples

(a) Decrease 68 by 35%.

To decrease by 35%, multiply by = 0.65

$68 \times 0.65 = 44.2$

$$1 - \frac{35}{100} = 0.65$$

(b) I bought a car for $8500.

A year later its value has fallen by 27%.

What is its value now?

To decrease by 27%, multiply by = 0.73

$8500 \times 0.73 = \$6205$

$$1 - \frac{27}{100} = 0.73$$

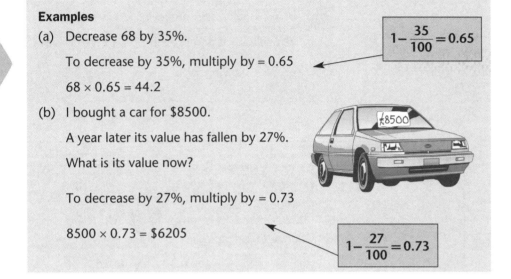

Reversed percentages

A washing machine costs $399.50, including VAT at 17.5%

$399.50 inc VAT

If you think that decreasing by 17.5% gives the answer, try working it back again.
399.50 × 0.825 = $329.5875
329.5875 × 1.175 = $387.27!

What was the price without VAT?

The cost without VAT was multiplied by 1.175 to give $399.50.

Use the inverse operation. Divide $399.5 by 1.175, which gives $340.

> **KEY POINT**
>
> To find the value before a percentage increase, divide by (1 + the percentage divided by 100).
> To find the value before a percentage decrease, divide by (1 – the percentage divided by 100).

> The amount was multiplied by 1.05, so divide 472.50 by 1.05.

> The amount was multiplied by 0.65, so divide 64.35 by 0.65.

Examples

(a) What amount, when increased by 5% gives £472.50?

$$472.5 \div 1.05 = £450$$

(b) In a sale, all prices are reduced by 35%.

The sale price of a dress is £64.35. What was the original price?

$$64.35 \div 0.65 = £99$$

PROGRESS CHECK

1 Change to fractions:
   (a) 30%   (b) $33\frac{1}{3}$%   (c) 85%   (d) 210%

2 Change to decimals:
   (a) 20%   (b) 43%   (c) $17\frac{1}{2}$%   (d) 155%

3 Change to percentages:
   (a) $\frac{3}{4}$ (b) $\frac{19}{20}$ (c) 0.37   (d) 0.015

4 Find:
   (a) 20 as a percentage of 50   (b) 7 as a percentage of 35
   (c) 18 as a percentage of 73

5 Find:
   (a) 18% of 73   (b) 6.8% of 142   (c) 0.45% of 100

6 Increase:
   (a) 83 by 20%   (b) 65 by 95%   (c) 1890 by 7.5%

7 Decrease:
   (a) 47 by 70%   (b) 195 by 17%   (c) 4.7 by 5%

8 Find:
   (a) what was increased by $17\frac{1}{2}$% to give £28.20
   (b) what was increased by 6.5% to give £1597.50
   (c) what was decreased by 25% to give £12 375
   (d) what was decreased by 2.5% to give 83.85?

> You should attempt some of these questions without a calculator as practice for the examination

8 (a) £24   (b) £1500   (c) £16 500   (d) 86
7 (a) 14.1   (b) 161.85   (c) 4.465
6 (a) 99.6   (b) 126.75   (c) 2031.75
5 (a) 13.14   (b) 9.656   (c) 0.45
4 (a) 40%   (b) 20%   (c) 24.7%
3 (a) 75%   (b) 95%   (c) 37%   (d) 1.5%
2 (a) 0.2   (b) 0.43   (c) 0.175   (d) 1.55
1 (a) $\frac{3}{10}$ (b) $\frac{1}{3}$ (c) $\frac{17}{20}$ (d) $2\frac{1}{10}$ or $\frac{21}{10}$

1.6 Bank interest

LEARNING SUMMARY

After studying this section, you will be able to:
- **understand the terminology used (rate of interset, principal, amount)**
- **calculate simple interest**
- **describe the difference between simple and compound interests**

When money is deposited in a bank, or borrowed form it, **interest** is paid (or charged) at a percentage rate.

The money put into the bank is called the **capital**, or **principal**. The **rate of interest** is given usually as a percentage per annum (or per year).

If we know the time for which the principal is invested, we can calculate the interest in two ways, depending on whether we are dealing with **simple** interest or **compound** interest.

KEY POINT

For simple interest, we use the formula

$$I = \frac{PRT}{100}$$

where *I* = Interest, *P* = Principal, *R* = Rate, *T* = Time.

For example, if **$3,000** is invested for 6 years at 4% per year, then interest can be calculated as follows:

Here, P = $3,000, R = 4, T = 6, so:

$$I = \frac{3,000 \times 4 \times 6}{100} = \$720.$$

The interest plus principal payable at the end is called the **amount**. Here the amount after 6 years is $3,000 + $720 = $3,720.

If we are dealing with **compound interest**, then the interest is added annually to the principal and we need to calculate year by year.

Example

Find the amount after 3 years, if $2,000 is invested at 10% compound interest.

We proceed as follows.
Year 1: P = $2,000, R = 10%, so interest after the first year is 10% of $2,000 = 200. So amount = $2,200.
Year 2: P = $2,200, R = 10%, so interest after the second year is 10% of $2,200 = $220. So amount = $2,420.
Year 3: P = $2,420, R = 10%, so interest after the third year is 10% of $2420 = $242. So amount = $2,662.

1.7 Ratio

LEARNING SUMMARY

After studying this section, you will be able to:

- **simplify ratios**
- **divide in a ratio**

Simplifying ratios

KEY POINT   A ratio compares the relative sizes of two or more quantities.

This is usually written
5 : 2

For example, the ratio of the number of days in the week to the number of days at the weekend is **5** to **2**.

Ratios behave in a similar way to fractions.

For example, I mix a drink with 40 ml concentrate and 240 ml water.

The ratio is **40 : 240 = 1 : 6**   ← | Divide each number by 40.

Example

Write these ratios in their simplest form.

| Divide each number in the ratio by the HCF.

2 : 8, 5 : 30, 20 : 70, 81 : 18

2 : 8 = 1 : 4, 5 : 30 = 1 : 6, 20 : 70 = 2 : 7, 81 : 18 = 9 : 2.

Dividing in a ratio

KEY POINT   To divide in a ratio, add the parts of the ratio to give the denominators of the required fractions. Each part of the ratio gives the numerators and the resulting fractions are multiplied by the quantity to be divided.

For example, if **50** is to be divided in the ratio **3 : 7**, there are **3 + 7 = 10** parts.

The first share is therefore $\frac{3}{10}$ of the **50**, that is $\frac{3}{10} \times 50 = 15$.

Examples

(a) Divide 75 in the ratio 3 : 2.

$3 + 2 = 5$ so the fractions are $\frac{3}{5}$ and $\frac{2}{5}$.

$\frac{3}{5} \times 75 = 45, \frac{2}{5} \times 75 = 30$

(b) Share $2500 in the ratio 1 : 3 : 4.

Always check that the parts correctly add to the total; $312.50 + $937.50 + $1250 = $2500.

$1 + 3 + 4 = 8$ so the fractions are $\frac{1}{8}, \frac{3}{8}, \frac{4}{8}$.

The shares are

$$\frac{1}{8} \times 2500 = \$312.50, \quad \frac{3}{8} \times 2500 = \$937.50, \quad \frac{1}{2} \times 2500 = \$1250$$

(c) A sum of money is shared between Jane and Pat in the ratio 6 : 5. Pat receives $250. How much does Jane receive?

$250 is 5 parts, so 6 parts will be $250 \times \frac{6}{5} = \$300$

1 Simplify these ratios:
(a) $8 : 10$ (b) $100 : 75$ (c) $1\frac{1}{2} : 2\frac{1}{2}$ (d) $49 : 7 : 63$

2 Share in the given ratio:
(a) 72 in the ratio $4 : 5$ (b) 98 in the ratio $6 : 1$
(c) $600 in the ratio $5 : 4 : 6$

PROGRESS CHECK

2 (a) 32, 40 (b) 84, 14 (c) $200, $160, $240
1 (a) 4 : 5 (b) 4 : 3 (c) 3 : 5 (d) 7 : 1 : 9

1.8 Money

LEARNING SUMMARY

After studying this section, you should be able to:

● *convert one currency to another*

Most money systems have a unit of currency that is divided into a hundred subunits.

● there are a hundred cents in a dollar ($)
● there are a hundred cents in a euro (€)
● there are a hundred pence in a pound (£)
● there are a hundred paise in a rupee (Re)

However, converting between currencies depends on their relative value, which changes daily and (sometimes) even hourly.

This is usually written 5 : 2

We may be told that $1 = €0.88 and, hence to convert $50 to euros, we multiply to get $50 \times 0.88 = €44$. Similarly, to convert €60 to dollars, we divide to get:

$$\frac{60}{0.88} = \frac{6000}{88} = 68.18, \text{ or } \$68$$

(as banks, money exchange agents etc., round down to the nearest unit only).

Look at this chart:

€ 1	£ 0.644
	$ 1.318

(a) Convert € 40 to pounds, rounded down to the nearest pound.
(b) Convert $ 200 to euros, rounded down to the nearest euro.
(c) How much worth is one pound, in terms of dollars?

 PROGRESS CHECK

(a) € 40 = 40×0.644 pounds = £ 25.76 = £ 25.

(b) $200 = $\frac{200}{1.318}$ = 151.75 € = € 151.

(c) 1 dollar = $\frac{1}{1.318}$ = € 0.758 = 0.758 × 0.644 pounds,

i.e. $1 = £0.488.

1.9 Measures and time

 LEARNING SUMMARY

After studying this section, you should be able to:

● *explain the basic units to measure mass, length and time*

● *understand the conversion from bigger to smaller units*

● *calculate time using twelve-hour and twenty four-hour clocks*

Measures

In our daily life, we need to measure various quantities.

KEY POINT

The base unit of mass is the kilogram, kg.
The base unity of time is the second, s.
The base unit of length is the metre, m.

Area is measured in square metres, m^2.
Volume is measured in cubic metres, m^3.

Let's look at the unit of length, the **metre**. An average person is between 1.5 and 1.9 metres tall. If we want to measure something really large, such as the distance between Tokyo and Los Angeles, we need to use a bigger unit – the **kilometre** (which equals 1000 metres) or even the **megametre** (which equals 1,000,000 metres).

If we want to measure something very small, we need a smaller unit. A pencil may be 12 cm (centimetres) long – a **centimetre** is a hundredth of a metre, just as a cent is a hundredth of dollar.

A human hair is less than a millimetre thick – a **millimetre** is one-thousandth of a metre.

Look at this staircase:

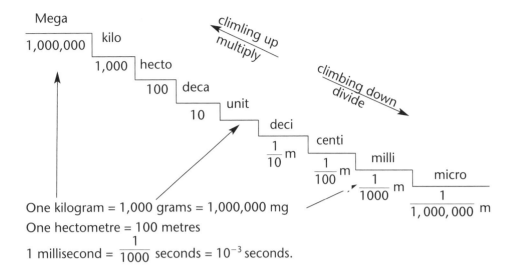

One kilogram = 1,000 grams = 1,000,000 mg

One hectometre = 100 metres

1 millisecond = $\dfrac{1}{1000}$ seconds = 10^{-3} seconds.

How many micrometres in a kilometre?

To climb from micrometres to metres , we multiply by 1,000,000.

To climb again from metres to km, we multiply by 1,000.

So $\qquad\qquad$ 1 km = 1,000,000,000 = $10^9\ \mu$ m.

Time

Time can be expressed in the **twelve-hour clock** (where the suffixes a.m. and p.m. are used), or in the twenty-four hour clock (where a four-digit number is used with no suffixes except the abbreviation hrs). The **twenty-four hour clock** runs from 0000 hours (which is midnight or 00.00 a.m.) until 2359 hours (which is 11.59 p.m.).

> There is no time represented by 2400 hours.

For example:

10.53 a.m. converts simply to 1053 hrs. and 1.25 p.m. becomes 1325 hrs.

Examples

Here is a bus timetable from START TOWN to END PLACE:

Start Town:	7.30 a.m.	8.50 a.m.	11.54 a.m.	11.48 p.m.
First Stop	7.43	9.03	12.07 p.m.	11.59 p.m.
Middle Stop	7.52	9.12	12.18 p.m.	00.09 a.m.
Third Stop	7.59	9.19	12.24 p.m.	00.16 a.m.
End Place	8.05	9.25	12.34 p.m.	00.20 a.m.

(a) Which journey takes the longest?

(b) Write down, in the 24 hour clock system, the time when the last bus reaches the first stop.

(a) We need to subtract the time the bus leaves Start Town from the time it reaches End Place in each case:

Bus 1: 8.05

$\qquad\quad$ −7.30

> **Since 30 is greater than 05, we need to borrow an hour and convert it into 60 minutes.**

Hence, we get: 7.65
                  −7.30
                  ‾‾‾‾
                   0.35.   So, this trips takes 35 minutes.

Bus 2: $\dfrac{9.25}{-8.50} = \dfrac{8.85}{-8.50}$

                   0.35   Again, the journey takes 35 minutes.

Bus 3: $\dfrac{9.25}{-8.50} = \dfrac{8.85}{-8.50}$

                   0.40   This trip takes 40 minutes.

Bus 4: $\dfrac{00.20}{-11.48} = \dfrac{11.80}{-11.48}$ ←———— | **Remember: − 1 hour from midnight is 11 p.m.** |

                   0.32

Bus 4 takes 32 minutes, so the longest journey time is that for Bus 3.

(b) The last bus reaches First stop at 2359 hours.

1.10 Mental methods

 LEARNING SUMMARY

After studying this section, you will be able to:

- *recall number facts*
- *round numbers*
- *make estimates*
- *give appropriate upper and lower bounds to given data and solutions of simple problems*

Recall

You should be able to recall many number facts, from easy ones like $8 + 7 = 15$ and $8 \times 7 = 56$, which you already know, to more difficult ones you may need to learn.

 KEY POINT

You should know:

- **All integer squares from $2^2 = 4$ up to $15^2 = 225$**
- **The square roots of the perfect squares from 1 to 225**
- **Integer cubes $2^3 = 8$, $3^3 = 27$, $4^3 = 64$, $5^3 = 125$ and $10^3 = 1000$**
- **The cube roots of 8, 27, 64, 125 and 1000**

Rounding numbers

KEY POINT

Numbers are rounded for two main reasons:
- **they are measurements and cannot be exact**
- **the accuracy of the discarded figures is not required.**

For example, you measure a length of a straight line with a ruler and find that it is **5.8 cm**.

A more accurate measuring instrument might give a value **5.84 cm** but greater accuracy, such as **5.837 924**, could not be attempted.

The number **5.84** is correct to two decimal places.

Examples
Write these numbers to the given accuracy:

5 or larger in the next place, round up.

(a) 15.78 correct to one decimal place

(b) 0.0345 correct to three decimal places

(c) 45 291 correct to the nearest hundred

(a) 15.8   (b) 0.035   (c) 45300

Rounding to a number of decimal places is not the only way.
This is the same measurement, made to the same accuracy,

4236.7 mm, 423.67 cm, 4.2367 m, 0.004 236 7 km

They each have a different number of decimal places but the same number of **significant figures**, five.

KEY POINT

The number of significant figures is found by ignoring zeros, which merely denote the size of the number, and counting the other figures.

> Zeros between non-zero digits are significant.

For example, 23.78 has four significant figures,
0.000 164 has three significant figures,
1.006 has four significant figures,
49 060 has four significant figures.

> Don't be tempted to round part (c) in two stages — **1.0945 →** **1.095 → 1.10.**

> In part (d), the zero is retained to show that it is correct to three significant figures.

Example
Write these correct to the number of significant figures shown.

(a) 65.794 (three)   (b) 0.003 86 (one)   (c) 1.0945 (three)
(d) 21.96 (three)

(a) 65.8   (b) 0.004   (c) 1.09   (d) 22.0

Estimates

 KEY POINT To estimate the result of a calculation, round or approximate each number so that you can work it out in your head. Rounding to one significant figure is often best.

Example

Estimate the answers to these calculations.

(a) $421 \times (73.6 - 21.7)$

(b) $\dfrac{0.0256 \times 937.2}{84.07 \times 0.567}$

(c) $(1.834 \times 10^{-4}) \div (9.7 \times 10^{5})$

'$\approx$' means 'approximately equal'

(a) $421 \times (73.6 - 21.7) \approx 400 \times (70 - 20)$
$$= 400 \times 50$$
$$= 20\,000$$

Further approximation during the calculation is sometimes needed

(b) $\dfrac{0.0256 \times 937.2}{87.07 \times 0.567} \approx \dfrac{0.03 \times 1000}{90 \times 0.6}$

$$= \dfrac{30}{54}$$

$$\approx \dfrac{3}{5}$$

$$= 0.6$$

(c) $(1.834 \times 10^{-4}) \div (9.7 \times 10^{5}) \approx (2 \div 10) \times (10^{-4} \div 10^{5})$
$$\approx (2 \times 10^{-4}) \times 10^{-6}$$
$$= 2 \times 10^{-10}$$

PROGRESS CHECK

1 State correct to the number of decimal places shown:
   (a) 509.27 (one) (b) 0.2739 (two) (c) 43.797 (two)

2 State correct to the number of significant figures shown:
   (a) 847.239 (two) (b) 0.0736 (two) (c) 80.174 (three)

3 Estimate to one significant figure:

   (a) 983×23.1 (b) $0.0792 \div 4.21$ (c) $\dfrac{18.9 \times 53.2}{0.207}$

   (d) $(2.7 \times 10^{3}) \times (8.16 \times 10^{-2})$

3 (a) 20 000 (b) 0.02 (c) 5000 (d) 2×10^{2}
2 (a) 850 (b) 0.074 (c) 80.2
1 (a) 509.3 (b) 0.27 (c) 43.80

Limits of accuracy

Here is a rectangle with its sides measured to an accuracy of 0.1 cm.

8 cm

5 cm

We can write the length as (8.0 ± 0.1) cm.

> Note that there are same number of digits after the decimal point.

We can write the width as (5.0 ± 0.1) cm.

> **Remember: Anything above 0.5 (and 0.5 itself) is round up while anything smaller is round down.**

The upper bound for the width is 5.4999̇ cm, which we write as 5.5 cm.

The lower bound for the length is 7.5 cm, since all numbers below this will not round up to 8.0 cm.

For the width, the true measurements must lie between 4.5 cm and 5.5 cm.

For the length, the true measurements must lie between 7.5 cm and 8.5 cm.

The perimeter of the rectangle is 5 cm + 8 cm + 5 cm + 8 cm = 26 cm, which we write as (26.0 ± 0.4) cm, as each side is measured to an accuracy of 0.1 cm.

So, the perimeter lies between 25.6 cm and 26.4 cm. The lower bound for the perimeter is thus 25.55 cm and the upper bound is 26.45 cm.

PROGRESS CHECK

A field is rectangular; its length is 100 m and its width is 85 m. All lengths are measured, correct to the nearest metre.

Write down the upper and lower bounds for the length, width and perimeter of the field.

	Upper Bound	Lower Bound
Length (100 ∓ 1 m)	101.5 m	98.5 m
Width (85 ∓ 1 m)	86.5 m	83.5 m
Perimeter (370 ∓ 4) m	374.5 m	365.5 m

1.11 Written methods

LEARNING SUMMARY

After studying this section, you will be able to:

- calculate proportional change
- recognise irrational numbers

Proportional change

 KEY POINT

Proportional change is when a quantity is increased or decreased in a given ratio. This is achieved by using a multiplier.

For example, percentage increase is a proportional change.

Increasing by **50%** means multiplying by $1 + \dfrac{50}{100} = 1.5$.

This is the same as increasing in the ratio **1.5 : 1** or **3 : 2**.

> Turn the ratio into something : 1
> The left-hand side of the ratio will give the multiplier.

> It is better to use a fraction in this case to avoid awkward decimals.

Examples

(a) Increase 38 in the ratio 5 : 2.

Ratio 5 : 2 = 2.5 : 1, so multiplier is 2.5.

$38 \times 2.5 = 95$

(b) Decrease 900 in the ratio 2 : 9.

Ratio $2 : 9 = \dfrac{2}{9} : 1$, so multiplier is $\dfrac{2}{9}$.

$900 \times \dfrac{2}{9} = 200$

Irrational numbers

 KEY POINT

A **rational number** is one that can be written as a fraction with numerator and denominator both as integers.
An **irrational number** is one that is not rational, so cannot be written as a fraction.

Examples of rational numbers are $5 \left(= \dfrac{5}{1} \right)$, $0.75 \left(= \dfrac{3}{4} \right)$, $\dfrac{5}{11}$.

Examples of irrational numbers are $\sqrt{2}$, $5 + 2\sqrt{3}$, π.

KEY
POINT

Numbers like $5 + 2\sqrt{3}$ are called **surds**.

Are numbers like $\dfrac{1}{\sqrt{3}}$ and $\dfrac{5}{5 + 2\sqrt{3}}$ irrational?

Examples

> Multiplying top and
> bottom by $\sqrt{3}$ does
> not alter the size of
> the number.

(a) Show that $\dfrac{1}{\sqrt{3}}$ is an irrational number.

$$\frac{1}{\sqrt{3}} \times \frac{\sqrt{3}}{\sqrt{3}} = \frac{\sqrt{3}}{3} \text{ which is irrational.}$$

(b) Show that $\dfrac{5}{5 + 2\sqrt{3}}$ is an irrational number.

Expand these brackets:

$$(5 + 2\sqrt{3})(5 - 2\sqrt{3}) = 25 + 10\sqrt{3} - 10\sqrt{3} - 4\sqrt{3}\sqrt{3} = 25 - 12 = 13$$

> For a better
> understanding of why
> this works, see
> Chapter 2, section 1

$$\frac{5(5 - 2\sqrt{3})}{(5 + 2\sqrt{3})(5 - 2\sqrt{3})} = \frac{25 - 10\sqrt{3}}{13}$$

> Multiply top and
> bottom by $5 - 2\sqrt{3}$.

and this is an irrational number.

(c) $\dfrac{1 + \sqrt{2}}{1 - \sqrt{2}}$

$$\frac{(1 + \sqrt{2})(1 + \sqrt{2})}{(1 - \sqrt{2})(1 + \sqrt{2})} = \frac{3 + 2\sqrt{2}}{1 - 2}$$

> Multiply top and
> bottom by $1 + \sqrt{2}$.

$$= -(3 + 2\sqrt{2})$$

and this is an irrational number.

> PROGRESS
> CHECK

1 Change in the given ratio:
   (a) 18, 4 : 3
   (b) 500, 3 : 4
   (c) 0.6, 5 : 4

2 Show whether these numbers are rational or irrational:

   (a) $\sqrt{3} \times \sqrt{6}$

   (b) $\dfrac{1}{\sqrt{5}} \times \sqrt{20}$

   (c) $\dfrac{1}{5 + 2\sqrt{2}}$

   (d) $\dfrac{4}{\sqrt{2} - 1}$

1 (a) 24 (b) 375 (c) 0.75
2 (a) $3\sqrt{2}$, irrational (b) 2, rational (c) $\dfrac{5 - 2\sqrt{2}}{17}$ irrational (d) $4 + 4\sqrt{2}$, irrational

1.12 Calculator methods

LEARNING
SUMMARY

After studying this section, you will be able to:

● **understand keys and display**
● **find upper and lower bounds**
● **understand exponential growth and decay**

Understanding keys and display

KEY POINT

Calculators are not all the same. You must learn how yours works.

> **You will also need sin, cos and tan for Chapter 3 and statistics keys for Chapter 4.**

For this section you need to use:

● **memory keys**

● **brackets**

● **power key** (sometimes labelled 'x^y') for proportional change and exponential growth.

● **the exponent key** (sometimes labelled 'EXP') to give standard index form and also interpret the display.

Upper and lower bounds

KEY POINT

**Measurements are not exact.
When a number is stated to a certain accuracy,
the greatest it could be is the upper bound
and the least it could be is the lower bound.**

For example, **234 mm** is correct to the nearest millimetre.

The upper bound is **234.5** and the lower bound is **233.5**, since if it were bigger than **234.5** it would be recorded as **235**.

Example

(a) The sides of a rectangle are measured as 12.7 cm and 35.8 cm, both to the nearest 0.1 cm. Find the upper and lower bounds of the area of the rectangle.

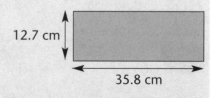

Bounds for the measurements are 12.65, 12.75, 35.75 and 35.85. The upper bound for the area will come from multiplying the upper bounds $12.75 \times 35.85 = 457.0875$ cm^2.

Similarly, the lower bound is $12.65 \times 35.75 = 452.2375$ cm^2.

(b) A car travels 5000 m, correct to the nearest metre, in 2 minutes 21.7 seconds, correct to the nearest tenth of a second.

Find the upper and lower bounds of the average speed in metres per second.

Bounds for the measurements are 4999.5, 5000.5, 141.65, 141.75.

The upper bound for the speed will come from the upper bound for the distance divided by the lower bound for the time,

$5000.5 \div 141.65 = 35.3018$ m/s.

Similarly the lower bound is $4999.5 \div 141.75 = 35.2698 \ldots$ m/s

> **The most accurate statement of the speed is 35.3 m/s**

Exponential growth and decay

> **KEY POINT**
>
> Exponential describes a situation when the variable is in the index.

For example, If the number of bacteria doubles every hour,
– then after one hour, multiply the starting number by **2**
– after 2 hours, multiply the starting number by $2 \times 2 = 2^2$
and so on.

This also applies to repeating proportional changes or percentage increases/decreases.

For example, $5000 is invested at **6.5%** compound interest for **5** years.

> With compound interest, the interest is added on and earns interest the next year(s).

After one year the amount is 5000×1.065.
After two years the amount is 5000×1.065^2
After five years the amount is $5000 \times 1.065^5 = \$6850.43$

> **This is where you need the power key on your calculator!**

> **PROGRESS CHECK**

1 Find the upper and lower bounds for $\dfrac{85.7}{183 \times 0.27}$.
   Each number is correct to three significant figures as shown.
2 A town has 47 000 inhabitants. It is growing by a factor of 1.2 a year. How many inhabitants will there be in 10 years time?
3 A substance of mass 200 g is decaying at a rate such that it will be $\dfrac{9}{10}$ of its mass at the end of the day.
   What will be the mass after 15 days?

3 41.2 g (to 3 significant figures)
2 291 000 (to nearest 100)
1 1.773 ... , 1.697 ...

1.13 Sets

LEARNING SUMMARY

After studying this section, you will be able to:

- *acquaint yourself with the set language and notation*
- *use Venn diagrams to solve problems*
- *understand the concept of subsets*

Defining a Set

A set is a collection of well-defined objects.

Look at these two statements:

1. 'The number of buildings, over 100 metres high, in New York.'
2. 'The number of tall buildings in New York'

Statement 1 is a set; we can measure all the buildings in New York and list those that are at least 100 metres high. All our lists should agree with each other, because all the *elements* (or items) in the set are *well-defined*.

Statement 2 is not a set, for we may argue about the meaning of the word 'tall'. The statement does not describe a collection of items that are well-defined. Sometimes we write sets by listing all the elements within 'curly' brackets:

{**red, orange, yellow green, blue, indigo, violet**} describes the set of colours in the rainbow.

We could have written the set as a rule, as follows:

$$\{x: x \text{ is a colour of the rainbow}\}.$$

Here, 'x' stands for all the elements that can be written down according to the specified rule. We read the set as follows:

$$\{x : x \text{ is a colour of the rainbow}\}$$

The set of elements x, *where* x is a colour of the rainbow.

Venn Diagram

Usually, we deal with sets of numbers and use capital letters to help us identify them:

$$A = \{\text{the set of prime numbers below 10}\}$$
$$B = \{\text{the set of odd numbers between 1 and 10, with end points inclusive}\}$$

We could list out the elements of set A as follows:

A = {2, 3, 5, 7} and we could draw the set on a Venn diagram:

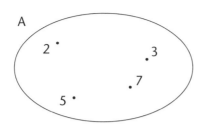

Since 2 is an element of set A, we write
2 ∈ A.
We could also write:
1 ∉ A, as 1 is not an element of A.

The Venn diagram for set B is:

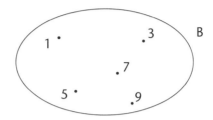

When A and B are drawn together on the same Venn diagram, they overlap and the elements that are common are placed in the overlapping, or **intersection** area:

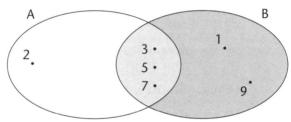

Now, notice these symbols and the explanations that follow:

A ∪ B = {1, 2, 3, 5, 7, 9}   A **Union** B,   means all the elements in A and B taken together.

A ∩ B = {3, 5, 7}.   A **Intersection** B,   means the elements that belong to both A & B.

We could write: 8 ∉ (A ∪ B),   because 8 is not an element of A and B taken together

7 ∈ (A ∩ B),   because 7 belongs to the intersection of both sets.

Sometimes, the sets we use are parts of a bigger set, known as **the Universal set**, denoted by a ξ.

Thus, if our universal set is:

ξ = {The whole numbers between 1 and 24, end points inclusive}

P = {The divisors of 24}

Q = {The even numbers between 2 and 14, including the end points}.

Here is the Venn diagram:

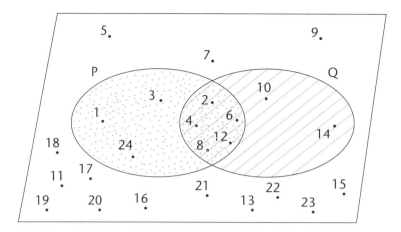

Also, P′ = the elements **not in P** and Q′ = the elements **not in Q**.

The number of elements in P, written as n(P) = 8, since P is the set {1, 2, 3, 4, 6, 8, 12, 24}.

Sometimes a set has no elements.

For example, G = {$x : x$ is a whole number between 3 and 4, end points exclusive}. Then G ={ } is the **null** set or empty set, often written as ϕ.

We can use Venn Diagrams to solve problems like this:
In a class of 30 students, 18 study history, 25 study geography and 2 study neither. How many study both the subjects?

Let H be the set of students studying history, G of those studying geography and ξ represent the whole class. We can draw the following diagram, assuming that x denotes the students who study both the subjects.

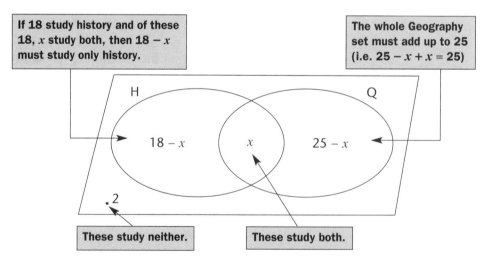

Now we know that the number of students in the class is 30. So, adding up all the expressions in the diagram, we have:

$$(18 - x) + x + (25 - x) + 2 = 30$$
$$\Rightarrow 45 - x = 30 \Rightarrow x = 15.$$

Hence, 15 students study both (and 3 study only history while 10 study only geography).

Subsets

A subset is a set that is part (or whole) of another set. Since all the elements in A = {3, 5, 6} are contained in B = {3, 4, 5, 6}, we say that A is a subset of B, written as **A ⊆ B**.

If P = {1, 2, 3}, then its subsets are:

$$\phi, \{1\}, \{2\}, \{3\}, \{1, 2\}, \{1, 3\}, \{2, 3\}, \{1, 2, 3\}$$

The first and last of these subsets, ϕ and P itself are included, but they are not *proper* subsets. The proper subsets are the other six, which contain *at least one and not all* of the elements of P.

The symbol for a proper subset is ⊂.

1.14 Solving problems

After studying this section, you will be able to:

- **consider strategies**
- **check your answers**

Strategies

Many problems are set in a way that the mathematics you need to solve them is clear — so long as you know it!

Others, sometimes called multi-step or unstructured, are not so obvious and may involve several steps to be identified. All IGCSE papers now contain some of these.

Before starting a problem like this, consider all the methods you know which may be relevant and then select the most appropriate.

Checking

It is important to check your work for mistakes.

It is especially true for answers derived from the calculator.

KEY POINT

You do not need to do all of these every time.

Always check a calculator answer by
- **considering if it is reasonable**
- **doing it again**
- **starting with your answer, use inverse operations to go back to the starting number.**
- **doing an approximate calculation.**

Number

PROGRESS
CHECK

1 (a) How many steps of 900 mm must you make in one minute to walk at 7 km/hour?

(b) At what speed will you walk if the step is shortened by 25 mm but you take the same number of steps in a minute?

2 A shopkeeper makes a profit of 40% on his cost prices.

He increases his selling prices by 10% but allows a 5% discount for cash.

(His cost prices stay the same.)

What is his percentage profit on cash sales?

1 (a) 130 (b) 6.8(25) km/hour
2 46.3%

Sample IGCSE questions

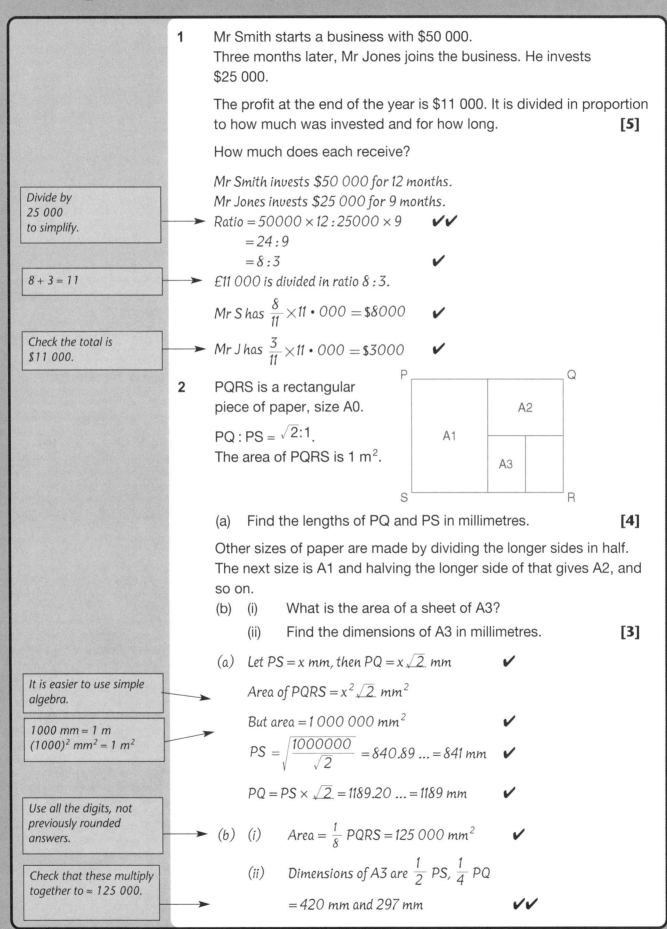

1 Mr Smith starts a business with $50 000.

Three months later, Mr Jones joins the business. He invests $25 000.

The profit at the end of the year is $11 000. It is divided in proportion to how much was invested and for how long. **[5]**

How much does each receive?

Mr Smith invests $50 000 for 12 months.
Mr Jones invests $25 000 for 9 months.

Divide by 25 000 to simplify.

Ratio = 50000 × 12 : 25000 × 9 ✔✔
$$= 24 : 9$$
$$= 8 : 3$$ ✔

8 + 3 = 11

£11 000 is divided in ratio 8 : 3.

Mr S has $\frac{8}{11} \times 11 \cdot 000 = \$8000$ ✔

Check the total is $11 000.

Mr J has $\frac{3}{11} \times 11 \cdot 000 = \$3000$ ✔

2 PQRS is a rectangular piece of paper, size A0.

$PQ : PS = \sqrt{2}:1$.
The area of PQRS is 1 m^2.

(a) Find the lengths of PQ and PS in millimetres. **[4]**

Other sizes of paper are made by dividing the longer sides in half. The next size is A1 and halving the longer side of that gives A2, and so on.

(b) (i) What is the area of a sheet of A3?

(ii) Find the dimensions of A3 in millimetres. **[3]**

(a) *Let PS = x mm, then PQ = x* $\sqrt{2}$ *mm* ✔

It is easier to use simple algebra.

Area of PQRS = x^2 $\sqrt{2}$ *mm*^{2}

1000 mm = 1 m
(1000)^2 mm^2 = 1 m^2

But area = 1 000 000 mm^2 ✔

$$PS = \sqrt{\frac{1000000}{\sqrt{2}}} = 840.89 \ldots = 841 \, mm$$ ✔

$$PQ = PS \times \sqrt{2} = 1189.20 \ldots = 1189 \, mm$$ ✔

Use all the digits, not previously rounded answers.

(b) (i) *Area =* $\frac{1}{8}$ *PQRS = 125 000 mm*^{2} ✔

Check that these multiply together to ≈ 125 000.

(ii) *Dimensions of A3 are* $\frac{1}{2}$ *PS,* $\frac{1}{4}$ *PQ*

$$= 420 \, mm \text{ and } 297 \, mm$$ ✔✔

Sample IGCSE questions

3 The number of members in a club decreases by 5% every year. This year there are 120 members.

(a) How many will there be in 10 years time? **[3]**

(b) How many were there five years ago? **[2]**

It is appropriate to round down. Can you see why?

Don't be tempted to multiply by $(1.05)^5$. Division is the inverse of multiplication.

Check this answer by multiplying by $(0.95)^5$ to give 120.

(a) *5% decrease gives multiplier $1 - 0.05 = 0.95$* ✔
$120 \times (0.95)^{10}$ ✔
$= 71.84 \ldots = 71$ ✔

(b) *$120 \div (0.95)^5$* ✔

$= 155.08 \ldots = 155$ ✔

4 Two accounts each contain $3000 earning compound interest. The interest rates are:

- Account A, 5% per annum
- Account B, 6% per annum (first two years), 4% per annum (third and subsequent years).

After four years, which account contains more and what is the difference? **[6]**

Multiplier 1.05 for four years.

First two years.

Second two years.

Account A: $3000 \times (1.05)^4$ ✔
$= \$3646.52$ ✔
Account B: $3000 \times (1.06)^2$ ✔
$\times (1.04)^2$ ✔
$= \$3645.86$ ✔
Account A contains more by 66p. ✔

5 Evaluate (do not use a calculator):

(a) $(27^{\frac{1}{3}})^2$ **[1]**

(b) $(1\frac{9}{16})^{-\frac{1}{2}}$ **[2]**

(c) $\frac{2}{3}\left(\frac{4}{7} - \frac{2}{5}\right)$ **[3]**

Fractional index means root.

(a) *$27^{\frac{1}{3}} = \sqrt[3]{27} = 3, \ 3^2 = 9$* ✔

(b) *$1\frac{9}{16} = \frac{16+9}{16} = \frac{25}{16}$* ✔

Negative index means reciprocal.

$\left(\frac{25}{16}\right)^{-\frac{1}{2}} = \frac{1}{\sqrt{\frac{25}{16}}} = \sqrt{\frac{16}{25}} = \frac{4}{5}$ ✔

Sample IGCSE questions

Brackets first.

$$(c) \quad \frac{2}{3}\left(\frac{4}{7} - \frac{2}{5}\right) = \frac{2}{3}\left(\frac{4\times5 - 2\times7}{7\times5}\right) \qquad ✔$$

Cancel by 3.

$$= \frac{2}{3} \times \frac{6}{35} \qquad ✔$$

Multiply numerators and denominators.

$$= \frac{4}{35}$$

6 Evaluate:

(a) $\dfrac{(18.7 - 15.3)^2}{18.7 \times 15.3} - \dfrac{(0.037 - 0.089)^2}{0.037 \times 0.089}$ **[2]**

Use memory.

(b) $\sqrt[3]{\dfrac{193.6 \times 9.87}{2 \times \pi}}$ **[2]**

Take care when dividing by 15.3 and 0.089.

(a) $0.0404 ... - 0.8211 ...$ ✔

$= -0.7807(31702)$ ✔

There is no need to show intermediate answers. Keep all figures in the calculator until the end. Do not round and re-enter.

(b) $= \sqrt[3]{304.11...}$ ✔

$= 6.7248(23326)$ ✔

7 If ξ = {1, 2, 3, 4, 5, 6, 7, 8, 9, 10, 11, 12},

M = {all prime numbers between 1 & 12 inclusive}

N = {all odd numbers between 1 & 12 inclusive}

(a) draw a Venn diagram to represent the above sets.

(b) What is: (i) M∪N (ii) M∩N (iii) M^l (iv) n(N)?

(c) Write down a proper subset of (M∪N).

(a)

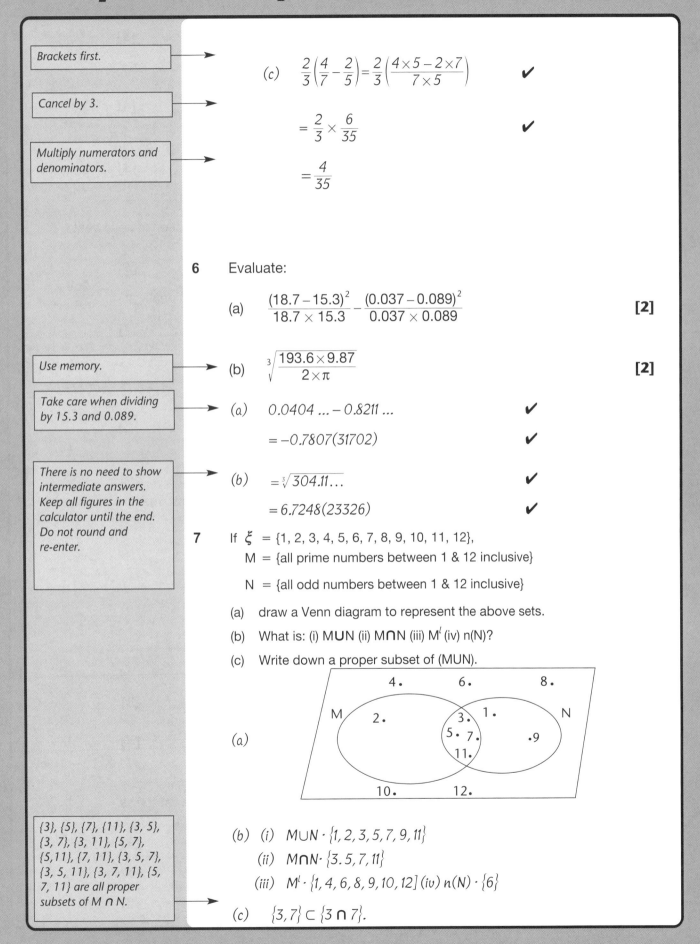

{3}, {5}, {7}, {11}, {3, 5}, {3, 7}, {3, 11}, {5, 7}, {5,11}, {7, 11}, {3, 5, 7}, {3, 5, 11}, {3, 7, 11}, {5, 7, 11} are all proper subsets of M ∩ N.

(b) (i) $M \cup N \cdot \{1, 2, 3, 5, 7, 9, 11\}$

(ii) $M \cap N \cdot \{3.5, 7, 11\}$

(iii) $M^l \cdot \{1, 4, 6, 8, 9, 10, 12\}$ (iv) $n(N) \cdot \{6\}$

(c) $\{3, 7\} \subset \{3 \cap 7\}.$

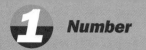

Number

Exam practice questions

1 (a) Write 1170 as a product of prime factors. **[3]**

(b) Simplify the following.

(i) $4^{-\frac{1}{2}} \times 8^{\frac{2}{3}}$ (ii) $\dfrac{\sqrt{3}}{9^{\frac{3}{4}}}$ **[4]**

(c) Find the value of this expression. Give your answer in standard index form.
$3 \times 10^{-2} + (4 \times 10^{-3}) \times (2 \times 10^{2})$ **[3]**

2 (a) Find the fractions equivalent to these decimals. Write each fraction in its lowest terms.
(i) 1.15 (ii) $1.\dot{1}\dot{5}$ **[5]**

(b) Simplify the following, showing whether each is rational or irrational.

(i) $(1+\sqrt{2})^2$ (ii) $(1+\sqrt{2})(1-\sqrt{2})$ (iii) $\dfrac{1}{1+\sqrt{2}}$ **[7]**

3 (a) A litre of petrol costs 79.9p, including VAT at 17.5%.
What is the cost before VAT is added? **[3]**

(b) Last year, petrol cost 69.9p (including VAT).

(i) What was the percentage increase? **[2]**
(ii) If this rate of growth continues, how much will a litre of petrol cost in five years' time? **[3]**

4 These data are from a car journey.

Average speed   90 km per hour (to nearest 5 kph)
Time taken   2 hours (to nearest 0.1 hour)
Fuel used   23 litres (to nearest litre)

Find:
(a) the maximum value of the distance travelled **[3]**

(b) the least value of the rate of fuel use (in litres per km). **[4]**

5 Calculate the following, giving yours answers as fractions in their lowest terms.

(a) $1\frac{2}{5} + 3\frac{3}{4}$ **[3]**

(b) $1\frac{2}{5} \times 3\frac{3}{4}$ **[3]**

(c) $3\frac{1}{3} - 2\frac{5}{6}$ **[2]**

Exam practice questions

6   If   A = {all the divisors of 16} and B = $\{2^0, 2^1, 2^2, 2^3, 2^4, 2^5\}$,

write down   (a) $A \cap B$
             (b) $A \cup B$
             (c) A'
             (d)   n(B)
             (e) B'.   **[5]**

7   If, for sets P and Q : P' = {3, 4}, P ∩ Q = {5, 6} and P ∪ Q = {1, 2, 3, 4, 5, 6}, draw a venn diagram representing the sets.   **[5]**

8   In a village of 290 families, 180 read 'The Times' and 135 read 'The Observer'. If 45 families read neither, how many read both the newspapers?   **[5]**

Algebra

Overview

Topic	Section	Studied in class	Revised	Practice questions
2.1 Symbols	Letter symbols			
	Manipulation			
	Know the words			
2.2 Index notation	Index laws			
2.3 Equations	Setting up equations			
2.4 Linear equations	Solving linear equations			
2.5 Formulae	Substituting into formulae			
	Changing subject of formulae			
	Generating formulae			
2.6 Direct and inverse proportion	Solving problems			
	Graphical interpretation			
2.7 Simultaneous linear equations	Solving simultaneous linear equations			
	Finding the solution on a graph			
2.8 Inequalities	Inequalities with one variable			
	Inequalities with two variables			
2.9 Linear programming				
2.10 Quadratic equations	Solving quadratic equations by factorising			
	Solving quadratic equations by completing the square			
	Solving quadratic equations by using the formula			
2.11 Numerical methods	Trial and improvement			
2.12 Sequences	Generating sequences			
	Finding the nth term			
2.13 Graphs of linear functions	Equations of straight lines			
	Parallel and perpendicular lines			
2.14 Interpreting graphical information	Graphs of real-life situations			
2.15 Functions and their graphs	Functions			
	Graphical solutions			
	Graphs of functions			
2.16 Transformation of functions	Transforming graphs			
2.17 Loci	Constructing loci			
	Graphs of circles			

2.1 Symbols

LEARNING SUMMARY

After studying this section, you will be able to:

- use letters as symbols
- manipulate algebraic expressions
- understand the meaning of the words used

Letter symbols

KEY POINT

Letters are used as symbols to represent:

unknown number(s) in an equation, which can be found, for example x in $x^2 + 3x + 2 = 0$
variables in formulae, which can take many values, for example $v = u + at$
numbers in an identity, which can take any values, for example $5(x - 2) = 5x - 10$, for any value of x

Manipulation

The rules for manipulating algebra are much like those in arithmetic.

For example,

$2a + 5a = 7a,\ b \times b = b^2$

$c^3 \div c^2 = c,$

$2d\,(3d - 7) = 6d^2 - 14d.$

> Remember the conventions:
> $y \times 2 = 2y$ rather than $y2$, which could be confused with y^2, coming from $y \times y$.

This leads to more complicated examples.

> Every term in one bracket must be multiplied by every term in the other. You can only collect like terms.

Examples

$(a + b)(c + d) = a(c + d) + b(c + d) = ac + ad + bc + bd$

$(x - 5)(x + 2) = x(x + 2) - 5(x + 2) = x^2 + 2x - 5x - 10 = x^2 - 3x - 10$

This process can be reversed. It is called factorising.

For example,

$12y^2 - 6y = 6y\,(2y - 1)$ ⟵   Each term can be divided by $6y$, so $6y$ is a factor.

Example

$x^2 + 5x + 6 = (x + 2)(x + 3)$

How did that happen?

You could work it out by trial and error, using your experience of expanding brackets.

A more systematic approach will save time!

Look at what happens when the brackets are expanded.

$(x + 2)(x + 3) = x^2 + 3x + 2x + 6$.

If it was given in this form you could spot the factors.

$x(x + 3) + 2(x + 3)$, which is $(x + 2)(x + 3)$.

| $2 + 3 = 5$, $2 \times 3 = 6$ |

Can you see how the 2 and the 3 combined to give 5 and 6?

> **KEY POINT**
>
> To factorise $x^2 + px + q$, find two numbers that will add to give **p** and multiply to give **q**.

The quadratic expressions will not always have plus signs.

For example,

$y^2 - 6y + 9$

The +**9** could result from multiplying two positive numbers but what about the **−6**?

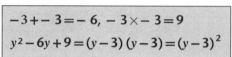

| $-3 + -3 = -6$, $-3 \times -3 = 9$ |
| $y^2 - 6y + 9 = (y - 3)(y - 3) = (y - 3)^2$ |

Of course, **9** also equals -3×-3 or -1×-9. Try these.

> **KEY POINT**
>
> To factorise $x^2 + px + q$, find two numbers that will add to give p and multiply to give q.
> This still works if p is a negative number.

Now try to factorise $x^2 - 3x - 10$.

Start with the −10. It could be −1 × 10, 1 × −10, −2 × 5, 2 × −5.

Notice that the signs are different, one positive and other negative.

Try the first:

$(x - 1)(x + 10) = x^2 - x + 10x - 10$

| $2 + -5 = -3$, $2 \times -5 = -10$ |

The two x terms have a different sign so they are subtracted. $10 - 1 = 9$, $1 - 10 = -9$, $-2 + 5 = 3$, so

$x^2 - 3x - 10 = (x + 2)(x - 5)$

> **KEY POINT**
>
> To factorise $x^2 + px + q$, when q is negative and p is positive or negative, find two numbers that will add to give p and multiply to give q.
> This still works so long as you remember the signs.

Know the words

These words are used in algebra:

Expression – any arrangement of letter symbols and possibly numbers.

Formula – connects two expressions containing variables, the value of one variable depending on the values of the others. It must have an equals sign.

Equation – connects two expressions involving definite unknown quantities. It also has an equals sign.

Identity – connects expressions involving unspecified numbers. An identity remains true whatever numerical values replace the letter symbols. It has a '≡' sign.

Function – a relationship between two sets of values such that a value from the first set maps on to a unique value in the second set.

PROGRESS CHECK

1 Simplify:
(a) $7a - 4b + 2a + 5b$ (b) $\dfrac{6ab}{2b^2}$ (c) $2x^2 + 3xy - 4y^2 + 2xy - 3x^2 + y^2$

2 Expand the brackets and simplify, if possible.
(a) $3x(5x - 7)$ (b) $(y + 4)(y - 3)$ (c) $(2x - 7)(5x - 3)$

3 Factorise:
(a) $x^2 + 7x + 12$ (b) $x^2 - 8x + 16$ (c) $y^2 - y - 20$ (d) $y^2 - 36$

3 (a) $(x + 3)(x + 4)$ (b) $(x - 4)^2$ (c) $(y - 5)(y + 4)$ (d) $(y - 6)(y + 6)$
2 (a) $15x^2 - 21x$ (b) $y^2 + y - 12$ (c) $10x^2 - 41x + 21$
1 (a) $9a + b$ (b) $\dfrac{3a}{b}$ (c) $5x^2 + 5xy - 3y^2$

2.2 Index notation

LEARNING SUMMARY

After studying this section, you will be able to:

- *do multiplication and division and find roots using indices*

Index laws

The index laws are the same as in Chapter 1.
Here is a reminder.

KEY POINT

The index law for multiplication and division: $a^p \times a^q = a^{p+q}$, $a^p \div a^q = a^{p-q}$.
The index law for brackets: $(a^p)^q = a^{p \times q}$. The law for zero index: $a^0 = 1$.

The reciprocal index law: $\dfrac{1}{a^p} = a^{-p}$. The law for roots is: $\sqrt[n]{a} = a^{\frac{1}{n}}$.

PROGRESS CHECK

1 Simplify:
(a) $(a^2 b^4)^{\frac{1}{2}}$ (b) $(x^3 y^7)^0$ (c) $(a^{\frac{1}{3}} b^{\frac{3}{4}}) \times (a^{\frac{2}{3}} b^{-\frac{1}{4}})$

2 Simplify:
(a) $(x^{-3} y^4) \div (x^{-2} y^2)$ (b) $\dfrac{p^3 q^{-4}}{p^{-1} q^{-2}}$ (c) $\sqrt{\dfrac{a^5 b^6}{a^7}}$

2 (a) $x^{-1} y^2$ or $\dfrac{y^2}{x}$ (b) $p^4 q^{-2}$ or $\dfrac{p^4}{q^2}$ (c) $\dfrac{b^3}{a}$ or $b^3 a^{-1}$

1 (a) ab^2 (b) 1 (c) $ab^{\frac{1}{2}}$ or $a\sqrt{b}$

2.3 Equations

After studying this section, you will be able to:

- create an equation using symbols from given information
- set up an equation

Setting up equations

The information you are given will include an unknown quantity. Unless you are told otherwise, state which letter you will use to represent this quantity.

For example,

The angles round a point are $x°$, $2x°$, $(x + 50)°$ and $(x - 30)°$.

This time x is given.

The sum of the angles round a point is equal to $360°$, so the equation is

> Leave out the degree symbol as both sides are in degrees.

$x + 2x + (x + 50) + (x - 30) = 360$, which simplifies to $5x = 340$

PROGRESS CHECK

1 Find and simplify these equations.
   (a) The angles of a triangle are $y°$, $3y°$, $(60 - y)°$
   (b) The perimeter of a rectangle is 32 cm.
        One side is three times as long as another.
   (c) Brian is three times as old as Adrian.
        In five years' time, Brian will be twice as old as Adrian.

1 (a) $y + 3y + (60 - y) = 180$, $3y = 120$
   (b) Let shorter side be x cm: $2x + 6x = 32$, $8x = 32$
   (c) Let Brian be b years old and Adrian a years: $b = 3a$, $b + 5 = 2(a + 5)$

2.4 Linear equations

After studying this section, you will be able to:

- solve simple linear equations
- solve more complicated linear equations

Solving linear equations

> **KEY POINT** An equation has two parts separated by an equals sign. The arithmetic operations you perform on an equation must be the same for each part.

Some equations are very simple.

Always do the same operation on both sides of the equation.

Examples

(a) $5x = 100$

$x = 20$ ← Divide each side by 5.

(b) $x + 4 = 7$ ← Subtract 4 from each side.

$x = 3$

Some equations involve both the previous ideas.

Example

$2x - 5 = 11$ ← Add 5 to each side.

$2x = 16$ ← Divide each side by 2.

$x = 8$

More complicated equations can involve brackets, with the unknown on one side or both.

Check first to see if each side has a common factor. If it does, divide each side by the factor.

Examples

(a) $3(x - 5) = 7$ ← Expand the bracket.

$3x - 15 = 7$ ← Add 15 to each side.

$3x = 22$ ← Divide each side by 3.

$x = 7\frac{1}{3}$

(b) $5x + 2 = 3x - 7$ ← Subtract $3x$ from each side.

$2x + 2 = -7$ ← Subtract 2 from each side.

$2x = -9$ ← Divide each side by 2.

$x = -4\frac{1}{2}$

(c) $4(x + 3) = 3(2x - 1)$ ← Expand the brackets.

$4x + 12 = 6x - 3$ ← Add 3 to each side.

Don't forget the negative signs.

$4x + 15 = 6x$ ← Subtract $4x$ from each side.

$15 = 2x$ ← Divide each side by 2.

$x = 7\frac{1}{2}$

Some of the previous equations had solutions involving fractions. Some equations have fractions in them.

It is much easier to remove the fractions first, by multiplying each side by the lowest common multiple of the denominators of the fractions.

Example

$\frac{1}{2}(x - 3) = \frac{1}{3}(2x + 1)$ ← Multiply each side by 6.

$3(x - 3) = 2(2x + 1)$ ← Expand the brackets.

$$3x - 9 = 4x + 2 \quad \longleftarrow \quad \boxed{\text{Subtract } 3x \text{ from each side.}}$$

$$-9 = x + 2 \quad \longleftarrow \quad \boxed{\text{Subtract 2 from each side.}}$$

$$-11 = x \text{ or } x = -11$$

PROGRESS CHECK

1 Solve these equations.
   (a) Your equation in question 1(a) in the previous Progress Check (page 61).
   (b) Your equation in question 1(b) in the previous Progress Check.

2 (a) $3(x + 4) = 16$ (b) $2 - 5x = x + 14$ (c) $2(5x + 1) = 7x - 6$

3 (a) $\frac{1}{2}x = 40$ (b) $\frac{1}{4}(3x - 5) = 2x + 3$ (c) $3y + \frac{1}{2} = 4 + \frac{2}{3}y$

3 (a) $x = 80$ (b) $x = -3\frac{2}{5}$ (c) $y = 1\frac{1}{2}$

2 (a) $x = 1\frac{1}{3}$ (b) $x = -2$ (c) $x = -2\frac{2}{3}$

1 (a) $y = 40$ (b) $x = 4$

2.5 Formulae

LEARNING SUMMARY

After studying this section, you will be able to:

- ● *substitute numbers in formulae*
- ● *change the subject of a formula*
- ● *generate a formula*

Substituting into formulae

Replace the letters in the formula with the given numbers then do the arithmetic.

Example

$$s = ut + \frac{1}{2}at^2$$

Find the value of s when $u = 10$, $t = 5$ and $a = 0.27$.

$$s = 10 \times 5 + 0.5 \times 0.27 \times 5^2$$
$$= 50 + 3.375$$
$$= 53.375$$

Changing the subject of formulae

KEY POINT   When manipulating formulae, the rules are the same as for equations.

In the formula $s = ut + \frac{1}{2}at^2$, s is called the **subject** of the formula, since the formula is arranged to give s immediately on substitution. Changing the subject means rearranging the formula so that it has a different letter as the subject.

Examples

(a) Make u the subject of the formula

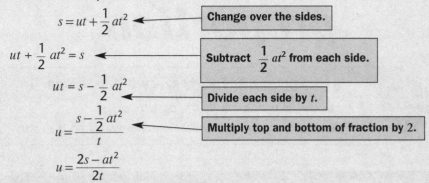

$$s = ut + \frac{1}{2}at^2$$ — Change over the sides.

$$ut + \frac{1}{2}at^2 = s$$ — Subtract $\frac{1}{2}at^2$ from each side.

$$ut = s - \frac{1}{2}at^2$$ — Divide each side by t.

$$u = \frac{s - \frac{1}{2}at^2}{t}$$ — Multiply top and bottom of fraction by 2.

$$u = \frac{2s - at^2}{2t}$$

> When the new subject appears more than once, make sure you collect those terms. Don't leave the 'subject' somewhere else in the formula.

(b) Make a the subject of the formula

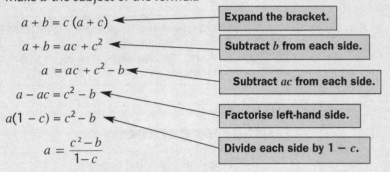

$$a + b = c(a + c)$$ — Expand the bracket.

$$a + b = ac + c^2$$ — Subtract b from each side.

$$a = ac + c^2 - b$$ — Subtract ac from each side.

$$a - ac = c^2 - b$$ — Factorise left-hand side.

$$a(1 - c) = c^2 - b$$ — Divide each side by $1 - c$.

$$a = \frac{c^2 - b}{1 - c}$$

Generating formulae

Instead of being given a formula, you may be asked to find one.

Example

A rectangle has perimeter P and one side is length L. Find a formula for its area A.

The area of a rectangle is its length multiplied by its width.

The length is L. The length plus the width is half the perimeter, so

width $= \frac{1}{2}P - L$.

So the formula is

$$A = L\left(\frac{1}{2}P - L\right)$$

PROGRESS CHECK

1 Substitute in these formulae.
   (a) Find v when $v = u + at$, and $u = 50$, $a = 10$ and $t = 2$.
   (b) Find s when $s = ut - \frac{1}{2}at^2$ and , $u = 0$, $a = -6$ and $t = 10$.
   (c) Find v when $v^2 = u^2 - 2as$ and $u = 13$, $a = 6$ and $s = 12$.

2 (a) Make a the subject of the formula $v = u + at$.
   (b) Make P the subject of the formula $A = L\left(\frac{1}{2}P - L\right)$.
   (c) Make t the subject of the formula $3t - s = t(s - 6)$.

3 (a) Find a formula for the area A of a circle with circumference C.
   (b) Find a formula for the surface area A of a cube with volume V.

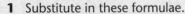

3 (a) $A = \frac{C^2}{4\pi}$ (b) $A = 6V^{\frac{2}{3}}$

2 (a) $a = \frac{v - u}{t}$ (b) $P = \frac{2(A + L^2)}{L}$ (c) $t = \frac{s}{s - 6}$

1 (a) $v = 70$ (b) $s = 300$ (c) $v = 5$ (or −5)

2.6 Direct and inverse proportion

LEARNING SUMMARY

After studying this section, you will be able to:

● solve problems involving proportion
● represent proportional relationships on a graph

Solving problems

KEY POINT

The symbol used to indicate **proportion** is $\propto$. So if y is directly proportional to x, write $y \propto x$.
This may also be expressed as an equation $y = kx$, where k is a constant.

Other proportions

y is inversely proportional to x: $y \propto \dfrac{1}{x}$

This is the range of what you are expected to know.

y is inversely proportional to the square of x: $y \propto \dfrac{1}{x^2}$

y is proportional to the square of x: $y \propto x^2$

y is proportional to the square root of x: $y \propto \sqrt{x}$

To solve a problem involving proportion, there are two main approaches. One is to change the relationship into an equation.

Example

The strength of a radio signal s is inversely proportional to the square of the distance d from the source. The strength is 8 when the distance is 5.
What is the strength when the distance is 50?

Using an equation

$s \propto \dfrac{1}{d^2}$, giving $s = \dfrac{k}{d^2}$.

When $d = 5$, $s = 8$, so $s = \dfrac{k}{25}$, giving $k = 200$.

When $d = 50$, $s = \dfrac{200}{50^2} = 0.08$

Another approach is to use multipliers.

For example, with the same problem.

Using multipliers

$s \propto \dfrac{1}{d^2}$ and d increases from **5** to **50**, that is by a multiplier of $50 \div 5 = 10$.

The multiplier for s is $\dfrac{1}{(\text{Multiplier for } d)^2} = \dfrac{1}{100}$

New value for $s = 8 \times \dfrac{1}{100} = 0.08$, as before.

Graphical interpretation

> **KEY POINT**
>
> **The graph representing a particular proportional relationship will be in the shape of the graph for the corresponding equation. The graph for y directly proportional to x will be $y = kx$.**

Other proportion graphs:

y is inversely proportional to x: $y = \dfrac{k}{x}$

y is inversely proportional to square of x: $y = \dfrac{k}{x^2}$

y is proportional to the square of x: $y = kx^2$

y is proportional to the square root of x: $y = k\sqrt{x}$

Sketch graphs like these do not need scales – or rulers!

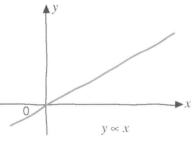

$y \propto x$

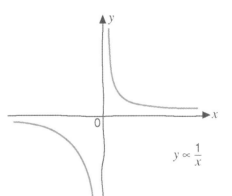

$y \propto \dfrac{1}{x}$

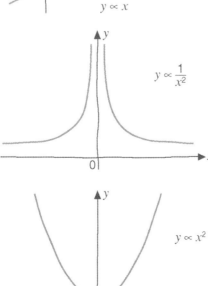

$y \propto \dfrac{1}{x^2}$

$y \propto x^2$

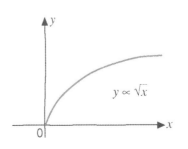

$y \propto \sqrt{x}$

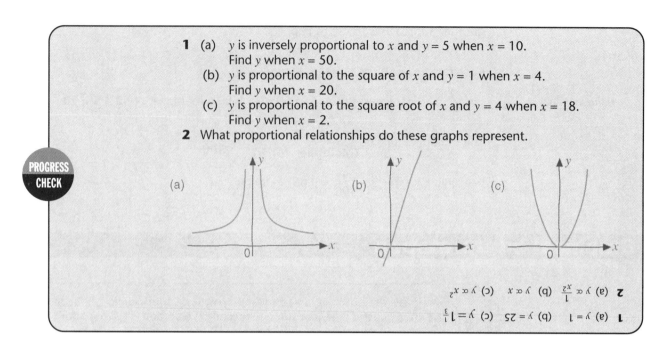

PROGRESS CHECK

1 (a) y is inversely proportional to x and $y = 5$ when $x = 10$.
Find y when $x = 50$.

(b) y is proportional to the square of x and $y = 1$ when $x = 4$.
Find y when $x = 20$.

(c) y is proportional to the square root of x and $y = 4$ when $x = 18$.
Find y when $x = 2$.

2 What proportional relationships do these graphs represent.

(a)   (b)   (c)

1 (a) $y = 1$ (b) $y = 25$ (c) $y = 1\frac{1}{3}$

2 (a) $y \propto \frac{1}{x^2}$ (b) $y \propto x$ (c) $y \propto x^2$

2.7 Simultaneous linear equations

LEARNING SUMMARY

After studying this section, you will be able to:

● **solve simultaneous linear equations by elimination**
● **solve simultaneous linear equations by substitution**
● **interpret the solutions graphically in terms of straight lines**

'Simultaneous' means 'taken together'.

Solving simultaneous linear equations

Two equations in two unknowns can have a unique solution. The first method to find this solution is called **elimination**.

Example

Solve

$$x + 2y = 7$$

$$4x - 3y = 6$$

$$4x + 8y = 28$$

$$4x - 3y = 6$$

$$\overline{11y = 22}$$

$$y = 2$$

$$x + 2 \times 2 = 7$$

$$x = 3$$

The object is to make either the x terms the same or the y terms the same. Multiply the first equation by 4.

Subtract the second equation from your new equation.

Divide each side by 11.

Substitute for y in the first equation.

Remember, when you subtract −3 it is the same as adding 3.

The solution is $x = 3$, $y = 2$.

The simultaneous equations can also be solved by writing one of the equations in the form '$x = ...$' or '$y = ...$' This is the second method and it is called substitution.

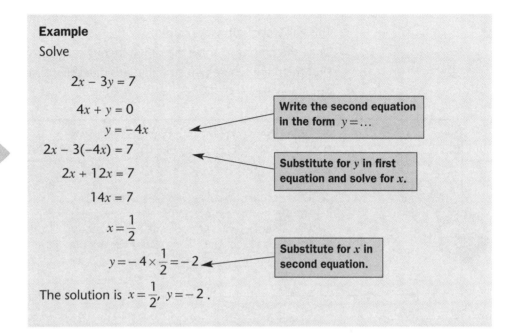

Example

Solve

$$2x - 3y = 7$$

$$4x + y = 0$$

$$y = -4x$$

$$2x - 3(-4x) = 7$$

$$2x + 12x = 7$$

$$14x = 7$$

$$x = \frac{1}{2}$$

$$y = -4 \times \frac{1}{2} = -2$$

The solution is $x = \frac{1}{2}$, $y = -2$.

> Write the second equation in the form $y = ...$

> Substitute for y in first equation and solve for x.

> Substitute for x in second equation.

> Take care with minus signs.

Finding the solution on a graph

An equation like $2x + 3y = 5$ can be represented on a graph. It will be a straight

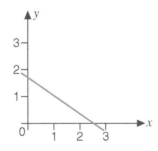

line (which is why it is called a linear equation).

The coordinates of any point on the line will satisfy the equation, that is the equation will be true when the coordinates are substituted for x and y.

The point (1, 1) is on the line and $2 \times 1 + 3 \times 1 = 5$.

Look at two straight lines drawn on the same axes. The equation of the other line is $x - 2y = -1$.

There is more about drawing graphs in Section 2.13 on page 64.

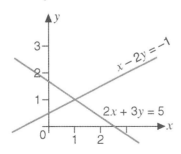

The point where they meet has coordinates that satisfy both equations.

> **KEY POINT**
>
> The coordinates of the **point of intersection** of two straight lines give the solution to the corresponding **simultaneous equations**.

This will work both ways round:

Draw the graphs to solve the simultaneous equations.

Find the point where two straight lines meet by solving their equations simultaneously.

PROGRESS CHECK

1 Solve these pairs of simultaneous equations:
   (a) $x + 2y = 1$, $2x + y = 5$ (b) $x + 2y = 6$, $3x - 6y = 12$
   (c) $3x - 2y = -9$, $4x + 5y = -\frac{1}{2}$

2 Draw graphs to solve these equations:
   (a) $x + y = 6$, $y = 2x$ (b) $x - y = -4$, $x + y = 2$

3 Use algebra to find the points of intersection of these lines:
   (a) $4x - y = 5$, $3x - 2y = 0$ (b) $6x - y = 4$, $4x + y = 1$

3 (a) (2,3) (b) $(\frac{1}{2}, -1)$

2 (a) $x = 2$, $y = 4$ (b) $x = -1$, $y = 3$

1 (a) $x = 3$, $y = -1$ (b) $x = 5$, $y = \frac{1}{2}$ (c) $x = -2$, $y = 1\frac{1}{2}$

2.8 Inequalities

LEARNING SUMMARY

After studying this section, you will be able to:

● *solve inequalities with one variable*
● *solve inequalities with two variables*

Inequalities with one variable

Example

Solve the inequality

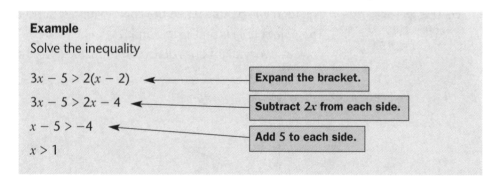

$3x - 5 > 2(x - 2)$ ← **Expand the bracket.**

$3x - 5 > 2x - 4$ ← **Subtract $2x$ from each side.**

$x - 5 > -4$ ← **Add 5 to each side.**

$x > 1$

> **KEY POINT**
>
> The rules for manipulating inequalities are like those for equations.

The next example is different.

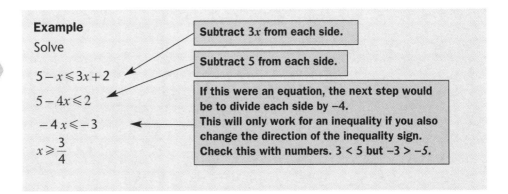

Sometimes the inequality includes equals. It is solved in the same way.

Example

Solve

$5 - x \leqslant 3x + 2$

$5 - 4x \leqslant 2$

$-4x \leqslant -3$

$x \geqslant \dfrac{3}{4}$

Subtract $3x$ from each side.

Subtract 5 from each side.

If this were an equation, the next step would be to divide each side by −4.
This will only work for an inequality if you also change the direction of the inequality sign.
Check this with numbers. 3 < 5 but −3 > −5.

KEY POINT

Manipulate inequalities like equations except that when multiplying or dividing each side by a negative number, change the direction of the inequality sign.

Inequalities with two variables

Here is an inequality in two variables.

$2x - y > 3$

This is similar to the equations in the previous section. The graph of $2x - y = 3$ is a straight line.

If you write the equation in the form $y = 2x - 3$, you can see that it crosses the y-axis at −3 and has gradient 2. (See Section 2.13.)

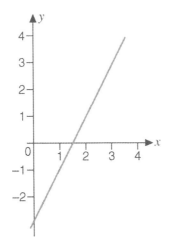

What is the value of $2x - y$ at a point above the line, say (1, 4)?
It is **−2**. Try a point below the line, say (4, −2). Here $2x - y = 10$.
Try other points and you will find that on the line $2x - y = 3$.
Above the line, $2x - y < 3$.
Below the line $2x - y > 3$.

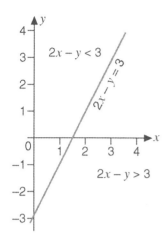

The solution to the inequality $2x - y > 3$ is a region. This is shown **unshaded** on the diagram.

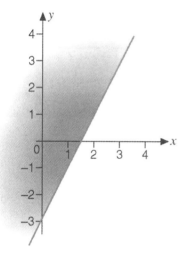

Several linear inequalities can be solved simultaneously.

Example

Show on a graph the solution set of the inequalities $2x - y > 3$, $x + y < 5$ and $y > 0$.

Shade out the unwanted regions.

A quick way to test which side of the line satisfies the inequality is to substitute (0, 0). It won't work for $y > 0$ though!

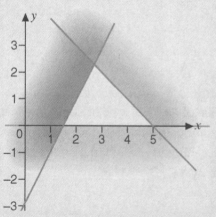

The solution set is the unshaded triangle.

PROGRESS CHECK

1 Solve these inequalities:
   (a) $2(3x - 7) > 5x - 3$ (b) $4 - 3x \leqslant 2x + 7$ (c) $3(3 - x) < 5(5 - x)$
2 Show the solution set for these inequalities on a graph:
   $x + y \leqslant 2$, $y - 2x \leqslant 5$, $x \leqslant 0$, $y \geqslant 0$

2 Quadrilateral with vertices $(0, 0)$, $(0, 2)$, $(-1, 3)$, $(-2\frac{1}{2}, 0)$

1 (a) $x > 11$ (b) $x \geqslant -0.6$ (c) $x > 8$

2.9 Linear programming

LEARNING SUMMARY

After studying this section, you will be able to:

● *represent inequalities graphically*
● *solve simple problems using linear programming*

Linear Programming is a useful method of analysing real business problems, especially in situations where profits are to be maximised or costs minimised. A set of conditions is converted to a series of lines, which are plotted on a graph; the points of intersection of these lines or '**boundary points**', are then analysed.

Let's look at the case of John, who owns an electrical shop where he sells television and hi-fi units.

To ensure an adequate supply of stock, the minimum quantities he keeps on the premises are 20 T.V.s and 30 hi-fis. Due to space restrictions, the total number of units he can stock cannot exceed 100.

When he sells a T.V., he makes a profit of $60; when he sells a Hi-Fi unit he makes a profit of $50.

Now, the question which arises is that what quantity of each item should John keep in stock to maximise his profit?

First, we represent number of T.V.s by the letter t, and number of hi-fis by the letter h.

Since John must beep a minimum of 20 T.V.s, $t \geqslant 20$, and since he must keep a minimum of 30 hi-fis, $h \geqslant 30$. Also, the total number of items must not exceed 100, thus $t + h \leqslant 100$.

These inequalities represent the **constraints**, or conditions that influence the solution. We plot these on a graph, as shown in the figure.

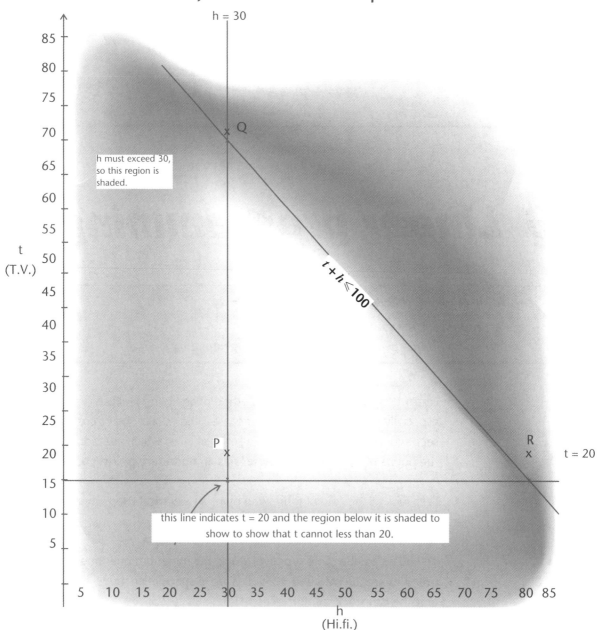

John's T.V. and hi-fi shop

On the graph, the central triangular portion has vertices labelled P, Q, R. These are the boundary points where the maximum or minimum possible values are to be found. Since John has a profit of $60 per T.V. and $50 per hi-fi:

P (30, 20) denotes a profit of $(30 \times 50) + (20 \times 60) = \$2700$,
Q (30, 70) denotes a profit of $(30 \times 50) + (70 \times 60) = \$5700$,
R (80, 20) denotes a profit of $(80 \times 50) + (20 \times 60) = \$5200$

Hence, Q denotes the point of maximum profit and John must carry a stock of 80 hi-fis and 20 T.V. sets.

Example

Annie makes pots. For her regular clients, her pottery must produce 20 large pots and 40 small pots everyday. It takes 6 minutes to produce a large pot and 4 minutes to produce a small one.

Her pottery shop runs for 8 hours each day.

She makes a profit of $1.80 on each large pot and $1.10 on each small pot.

(a) Write down three constraints in inequality form.

(b) What mix of items should Annie make, to maximise her profit?

(see graph below):

(a) Let l = number of large pots and s = number of small pots:

$l \geqslant 20$

$s \geqslant 40$

$6l + 4s \leqslant 480$, or $3l + 2s \leqslant 240$.

(b) $139.50, if Annie makes 50 large and 45 small pots.

KEY POINT

Since all the constraint inequalities include an equals sign (i.e. $\leqslant$ rather than $<$, and $\geqslant$ rather than $>$), the lines are drawn solid to show that points on the line are included in the solution. Otherwise, they would have been drawn as broken lines.

Annie's Pottery

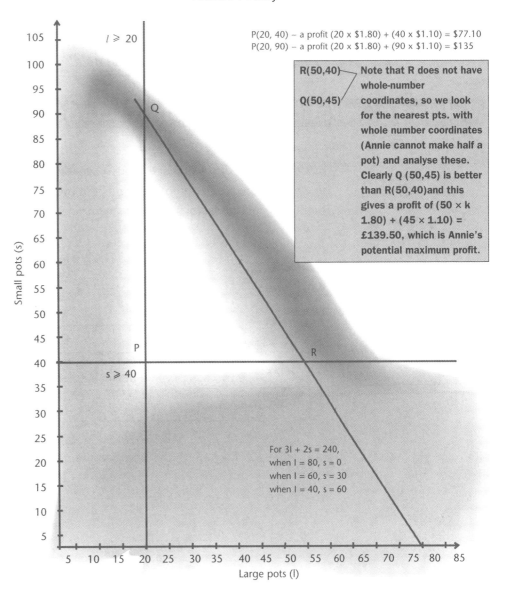

P(20, 40) – a profit (20 x $1.80) + (40 x $1.10) = $77.10
P(20, 90) – a profit (20 x $1.80) + (90 x $1.10) = $135

R(50,40)
Q(50,45)

Note that R does not have whole-number coordinates, so we look for the nearest pts. with whole number coordinates (Annie cannot make half a pot) and analyse these. Clearly Q (50,45) is better than R(50,40)and this gives a profit of (50 × k 1.80) + (45 × 1.10) = £139.50, which is Annie's potential maximum profit.

For 3l + 2s = 240,
when l = 80, s = 0
when l = 60, s = 30
when l = 40, s = 60

$l \geqslant 20$

$s \geqslant 40$

Small pots (s)

Large pots (l)

PROGRESS CHECK

1 Hawk motors produce two types of car – the Condor, which sells at a profit of € 2,800, and the Eagle which sells at a profit of € 3,600.

To produce a Condor car, 4 hours of assembly-line time is used, while an Eagle requires 6 hours to be manufactured.

Hawk motors are committed to producing 6 Eagles and 8 Condors each week, to fulfil ongoing orders.

What number of each car should be produced, if the factory has two assembly lines which run continuously from 6 a.m. Monday until 6 a.m. Saturday?

The factory should produce 6 Eagles and 51 Condors to show a potential profit of € 164,400.

2.10 Quadratic equations

LEARNING SUMMARY

After studying this section, you will be able to:

● *solve quadratic equations by factorising*
● *solve quadratic equations by completing the square*
● *solve quadratic equations by using the formula*

A quadratic equation is one that contains a term with the variable squared.

Solving quadratic equations by factorising

If the quadratic equation is on the non-calculator paper, it is worth looking for factors.

Quadratic expressions were factorised in Section 2.1.

For an equation, the first step is to write it in the form $ax^2 + bx + c = 0$.

Then try to find the factors of the left-hand side.

Examples

(a) Solve $x^2 - 3x + 2 = 0$.

> The two numbers are −1 and −2.

$(x - 1)(x - 2) = 0$

KEY POINT If two numbers are multiplied and the result is zero, then one or the other is zero.

Either $x - 1 = 0$ or $x - 2 = 0$, giving the solution $x = 1$ or $x = 2$.

(b) Solve $x^2 - x - 56 = 0$.

> The two numbers are 7 and −8.

$(x + 7)(x - 8) = 0$

Either $x + 7 = 0$ or $x + 8 = 0$, giving the solution $x = -7$ or $x = 8$.

Solving quadratic equations by completing the square

This is a different approach. Look at this example.

> **Example**
> Solve $(x - 3)^2 = 25$
> $$x - 3 = \pm 5$$
> The solution is $x = 8$ or $x = -2$.

> The only x term is inside the bracket to be squared. Taking the square root will leave just x and not x^2.

Don't forget the negative value of the square root.

Any quadratic equation can be rearranged so that it can be solved this way.

It will help to remember that
$$(x + p)^2 = x^2 + 2px + p^2$$
and
$$(x - p)^2 = x^2 - 2px - p^2$$

> **Examples**
> (a) Solve
> $$x^2 - 6x + 7 = 0$$
> $$x^2 - 6x = -7$$
> $$x^2 - 6x + 9 = -7 + 9$$
> $$(x - 3)^2 = 2$$
> $$x - 3 = \pm \sqrt{2}$$
>
> But $x^2 - 6x + 9 = (x - 3)^2$, so add 9 to each side.
>
> The solution is $x = 3 + \sqrt{2}$ or $x = 3 - \sqrt{2}$ (4.41 or 1.59 in decimals to 3 s.f.).
>
> (b) Solve
> $$2x^2 + 6x - 3 = 0$$
> $$x^2 + 3x = 1\tfrac{1}{2}$$
> $$x^2 + 3x + (1\tfrac{1}{2})^2 = 1\tfrac{1}{2} + (1\tfrac{1}{2})^2$$
> $$(x + 1.5)^2 = 3.75$$
> $$x + 1.5 = \pm \sqrt{3.75}$$
>
> Divide each side by 2.
>
> $x^2 + 3x + (1\tfrac{1}{2})^2 = (x + 1\tfrac{1}{2})^2$, so add $(1\tfrac{1}{2})^2$ to each side
>
> The solution is $x = 0.436$ or $x = -3.44$ to 3 s.f.

Solving quadratic equations by using the formula

If you apply the method of completing the square to the general equation $ax^2 + bx + c = 0$, you will obtain a formula for the solution of the equation. You do not have to find the formula for yourself and it can be quoted in an examination.

> **KEY POINT**
> The solution of the quadratic equation $ax^2 + bx + c = 0$ is given by
> $$x = \frac{-b \pm \sqrt{b^2 - 4ac}}{2a}$$

Try the formula on the earlier examples.

(a) $x^2 - 6x + 7 = 0$

$$x = \frac{6 \pm \sqrt{36 - 4 \times 7}}{2}$$

Solution is $x = 4.41$ or $x = 1.59$.

Great care is needed with the negative signs and getting the operations on your calculator in the right order.

(b) $2x^2 + 6x - 3 = 0$

$$x = \frac{-6 \pm \sqrt{36 - 4 \times 2 \times (-3)}}{2 \times 2}$$

Solution is $x = 0.436$ or $x = -3.44$.

PROGRESS CHECK

1 Solve these equations by factorising.
(a) $x^2 + 9x + 20 = 0$ (b) $x^2 - 4x - 45 = 0$ (c) $x^2 + 3x - 40 = 0$
(d) $x^2 - 7x + 6 = 0$
2 Solve these equations by completing the square.
(a) $y^2 - 8y + 3 = 0$ (b) $2y^2 + 10y - 9 = 0$
3 Solve these equations using the formula.
(a) $x^2 + 3x + 1 = 0$ (b) $3x^2 - 8x - 7 = 0$

3 (a) $x = -0.382$ or $x = -2.62$ (b) $x = 3.36$ or $x = -0.694$
2 (a) $y = 7.61$ or $y = 0.394$ (b) $y = 0.779$ or $y = -5.78$
1 (a) $x = -4$ or $x = -5$ (b) $x = 9$ or $x = -5$ (c) $x = -8$ or $x = 5$ (d) $x = 6$ or $x = 1$

2.11 Numerical methods

LEARNING SUMMARY

After studying this section, you will be able to:

● *solve equations that you cannot solve by simple manipulative methods*

Trial and improvement

Some equations cannot be solved in a simple way.
Here are two cubic equations.

$(2x + 1)(x - 3)(x - 5) = 0$

$x^3 + 2x - 1 = 0$

You will not be expected to find the factors of a cubic equation.

The first is in a factorised form and can be solved in a similar way to a quadratic equation. One of the factors, $(2x + 1)$, $(x - 3)$ and $(x - 5)$, must be zero so $x = -\frac{1}{2}$ or $x = 3$ or $x = 5$.
If the cubic equation cannot be factorised there is no easy formula for the solution.

However, it is possible to use an approximate method, which can be refined to any degree of accuracy required.

For example, in the second equation, when $x = 0$ the left-hand side is -1, which is less than 0;

when $x = 1$ the left-hand side is 2, which is greater than 0.

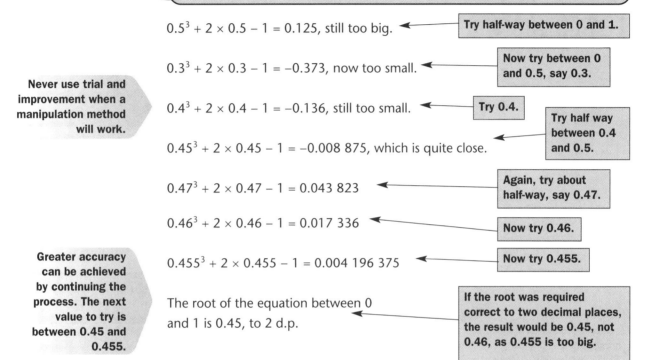

> **KEY POINT**
>
> The object of the method of trial and improvement is to systematically find a value of x which makes the expression $x^3 + 2x - 1$ as close as possible to 0. This value is called a **root** of the equation.

$0.5^3 + 2 \times 0.5 - 1 = 0.125$, still too big. ← Try half-way between 0 and 1.

$0.3^3 + 2 \times 0.3 - 1 = -0.373$, now too small. ← Now try between 0 and 0.5, say 0.3.

Never use trial and improvement when a manipulation method will work.

$0.4^3 + 2 \times 0.4 - 1 = -0.136$, still too small. ← Try 0.4.

← Try half way between 0.4 and 0.5.

$0.45^3 + 2 \times 0.45 - 1 = -0.008\ 875$, which is quite close.

$0.47^3 + 2 \times 0.47 - 1 = 0.043\ 823$ ← Again, try about half-way, say 0.47.

$0.46^3 + 2 \times 0.46 - 1 = 0.017\ 336$ ← Now try 0.46.

Greater accuracy can be achieved by continuing the process. The next value to try is between 0.45 and 0.455.

$0.455^3 + 2 \times 0.455 - 1 = 0.004\ 196\ 375$ ← Now try 0.455.

The root of the equation between 0 and 1 is 0.45, to 2 d.p. ← If the root was required correct to two decimal places, the result would be 0.45, not 0.46, as 0.455 is too big.

PROGRESS CHECK

1 Use the method of trial and improvement to find a root for each of these equations, correct to one decimal place.
   (a) $x^3 - 4x + 5 = 0$, between -3 and 2
   (b) $x^3 + x^2 + 3 = 0$, between 1 and 2   (c) $x^4 + 3x - 6 = 0$, between -2 and -1.

1 (a) -2.4 (b) 1.2 (c) -1.8

2.12 Sequences

 LEARNING SUMMARY

After studying this section, you will be able to:

- generate sequences of integers
- describe the nth term of a sequence

Generating sequences

 KEY POINT To generate a sequence, you need a **starting value** and a **rule** to find the next term.

For example,

Starting with **1**, add **2** each time.

This gives the sequence **1, 3, 5 ,7 ,9,**..., which are the odd numbers.

Here is another **example**.

Start with **1** again and now multiply by **2** each time.

This gives the sequence **1, 2, 4, 8, 16**, ..., which are the powers of 2.

 KEY POINT Sequences can also be generated from an expression for a **general term**, the **nth term**.

Here n stands for the number of the position in the sequence, so in the first position, $n = 1$, in the second $n = 2$, and so on.

For example,

if the **nth term** of a sequence is **$2n - 1$**, then the sequence is **1, 3, 5 ,7 ,9,**..., the odd numbers again.

Finding the nth term

Try some more sequences.

nth term = $n + 1$ gives 2, 3, 4, 5, 6 ...
nth term = $n - 3$ gives –2, –1, 0, 1, 2, ...

In each case the terms go up by one each time.

Now try these.

nth term = $2n + 1$ gives 3, 5, 7, 9, ...
nth term = $2n + 8$ gives 10, 12, 14, 16, ...

The difference is 2 each time.

nth term = $5n - 4$ gives 1, 6, 11, 16, 21, ...

The differences are now 5.

In algebra, a number which is the multiple of an unknown is called its coefficient. For example in the expression $2x^2 + 5x - 3$, the coefficient of x^2 is 2 and the coefficient of x is 5.

KEY POINT

If the differences between successive terms in a sequence are constant, this difference gives the coefficient of n in the expression for the nth term.

For example, to find the **nth term** of the sequence

3, 6, 9, 12, 15, ...

The differences are 3 each time, so the **nth term** involves $3n$.
Check to see that this is in fact the nth term.

Here is another **example**.
Find the nth term of the sequence

5, 9, 13, 17, 21, ...

The differences are 4 each time, so the **nth term** involves $4n$.
However, **$4n$** gives the sequence **4, 8, 12, 16**, ... which is always one less than the given sequence.
This means that the **nth term** is **$4n + 1$**.
Check to see that it works.

PROGRESS CHECK

1 Generate these sequences.
   (a) Start with –2 and add 5 each time.
   (b) Start with 50 and subtract 3 each time.
   (c) Start with 1 and multiply by 3 each time.
   (d) Start with 128 and multiply by $\frac{1}{2}$ each time.

2 Write down the first four terms of the sequences with these nth terms.
   (a) $4n - 3$ (b) $2n^2$ (c) $n(n + 1)$ (d) 2^n

3 Find the nth terms for these sequences.
   (a) 1, 4, 7, 10, 13, ... (b) 4, 6, 8, 10, 12, ... (c) –5, 0, 5, 10, 15, ...
   (d) 26, 25, 24, 23, 22, ...

3 (a) $3n - 2$ (b) $2n + 2$ (c) $5n - 10$ (d) $27 - n$
2 (a) 1, 5, 9, 13, ... (b) 2, 8, 18, 32, ... (c) 2, 6, 12, 20, ... (d) 2, 4, 8, 16, ...
1 (a) –2, 3, 8, 13, 18, ... (b) 50, 47, 44, 41, 38, ... (c) 1, 3, 9, 27, 81, ...
   (d) 128, 64, 32, 16, 8, ...

2.13 Graphs of linear functions

LEARNING SUMMARY

After studying this section, you will be able to:

- *recognise the form of the equation for a straight line*
- *find and interpret the gradients of straight lines*

The function is sometimes written as a mapping $f: x \rightarrow ax + b$.

KEY POINT

A function f of x is linear when $f(x) = ax + b$, where a and b are constants. The graph of the function $y = ax + b$ is a straight line.

Equations of straight lines

Draw the graph of $y = 3x + 1$.

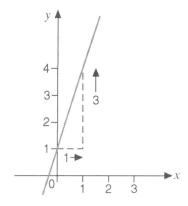

The gradient is found by dividing the increase in y values by the increase in x values.

The graph goes up to the right. For every unit it moves across, it moves 3 units up. The **gradient** of the line is 3.

It crosses the y-axis at (0, 1). This point is called the **intercept**.
Notice where the 3 and the 1 appear in the equation.

Now draw the graph of $y + 2x - 3 = 0$. This can be written as $y = -2x + 3$.

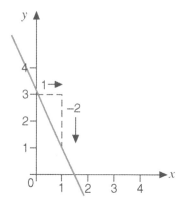

The gradient is negative since the y values decrease.

The graph goes down to the right. For every unit it moves across, it moves 2 units down. The gradient of the line is −2.

The line crosses the y-axis at (0, 3).

Notice where the −2 and the 3 appear in the equation.

> **KEY POINT**
> In the equation of a straight line $y = mx + c$, m is the gradient and c is the intercept on the y-axis.

Examples

Find the gradients and y-intercepts for these straight-line equations.

(a) $y = x - 1$ (b) $x + y = 5$ (c) $2y = x - 3$

(a) the gradient and intercept can be read directly from the equation. The gradient is 1 and the intercept is −1.

(b) $y = -x + 5$. Gradient is −1 and intercept is 5.

> Rewrite (b) in the form $y = mx + c$.

(c) $y = \frac{1}{2}x - 1\frac{1}{2}$. Gradient is $\frac{1}{2}$ and intercept is $-1\frac{1}{2}$.

> Divide each side of (c) by 2.

Parallel and perpendicular lines

Draw the graph of $y = 3x - 1$ on the same axes as $y = 3x + 1$.

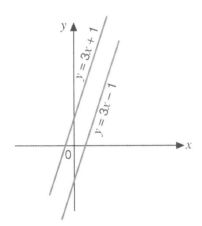

These lines are parallel. Try $y = 3x + 3$. Still parallel?

> **KEY POINT**
> Lines with equal gradients are parallel.

Now draw a straight line through (0, 1) perpendicular to the three lines.

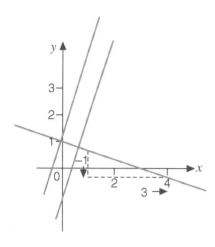

What is the gradient of this new line?

> The gradient is negative as the y-values decrease.

It goes down one unit for every 3 it moves across.

This gives gradient $-\frac{1}{3}$.

Multiply the gradients of the two perpendicular lines. Try this for more pairs of perpendicular lines.

KEY POINT

Multiplying the gradients of two perpendicular lines gives –1.

Examples

Find the gradient of a line perpendicular to $y = \frac{1}{2}x + 2$.

Let the gradient be m, then

$m \times \frac{1}{2} = -1$, giving $m = -2$.

PROGRESS CHECK

1 Find the gradients and y-intercepts of these lines.

    (a) $y = -\frac{1}{2}x + 3$ (b) $y = 4 - 2x$ (c) $2x - y = 1$ (d) $3y = 2x - 1$

2 Find the equations of these lines.

    (a)   Parallel to $y = 4x - 2$, through $(0, 3)$
    (b)   Parallel to $x + y = 5$ through $(0, -2)$
    (c)   Perpendicular to $y = 2x + 5$, through $(0, 4)$
    (d)   Perpendicular to $x + y = 5$, through $(0, -1)$

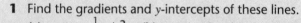

2 (a) $y = 4x + 3$ (b) $y = -x - 2$ or $x + y = -2$ (c) $y = -\frac{1}{2}x + 4$ or $2y + x = 8$ (d) $y = x - 1$

1 (a) $-\frac{1}{2}$, 3 (b) -2, 4 (c) 2, -1 (d) $\frac{2}{3}, \frac{-1}{3}$

2.14 Interpreting graphical information

LEARNING SUMMARY

After studying this section, you will be able to:

● *use and interpret graphs involving practical situations*

Graphs of real-life situations

The graphs in this section will show how quantities vary with time.

Examples

(a) This is a distance-time graph.

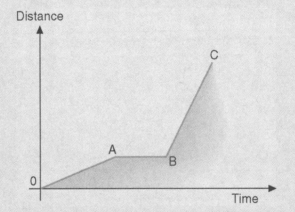

> The gradient of a distance-time graph gives the velocity (speed).

Look at each section.
From O to A, distance increases as time increases steadily. This is constant speed.
From A to B, the distance does not increase. The object is stationary.
From B to C, the speed is again constant but greater, as the gradient is greater.

(b) This is a velocity-time graph.

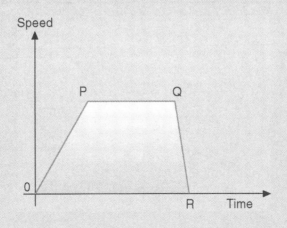

> The gradient of a velocity (speed) - time graph gives the acceleration.

Look at each section.

From O to P, the speed increases steadily. This is constant acceleration.

From P to Q, there is no increase in speed. There is no acceleration.

From Q to R, the speed decreases. This is negative acceleration or deceleration.

1 Interpret these graphs.

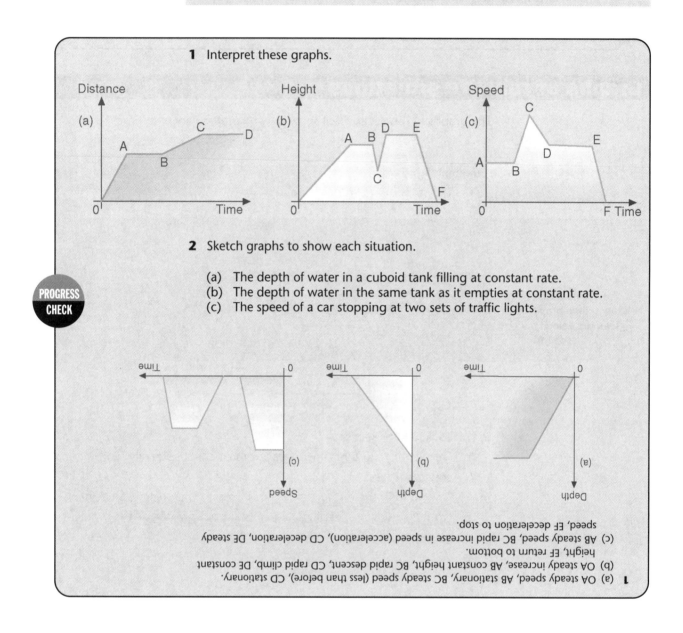

2 Sketch graphs to show each situation.

(a) The depth of water in a cuboid tank filling at constant rate.
(b) The depth of water in the same tank as it empties at constant rate.
(c) The speed of a car stopping at two sets of traffic lights.

1 (a) OA steady speed, AB stationary, BC steady speed (less than before), CD stationary.
(b) OA steady increase, AB constant height, BC rapid descent, CD rapid climb, DE constant height, EF return to bottom.
(c) AB steady speed, BC rapid increase in speed (acceleration), CD deceleration, DE steady speed, EF deceleration to stop.

2.15 Functions and their graphs

LEARNING SUMMARY

After studying this section, you will be able to:

● *use function notation*
● *understand the concept of inverse of function*
● *form composite functions*
● *solve equations using graphs*
● *draw the graphs of functions*

Functions

A function maps one set onto another by means of a rule. For instance, if one set is {**Dublin, Montreal, Brasilia, Paris**} and another set is {**Canada, Brazil, Ireland, France**}, then, using the rule 'is the capital of', we have this mapping:

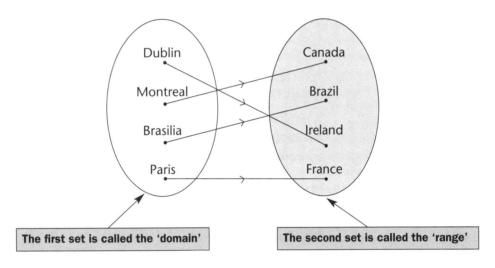

The first set is called the 'domain'

The second set is called the 'range'

While dealing with numbers, we use lower case letters to denote the function.

Example:

$g(x) = x^2 - 3$

'g' is a function that maps x to $x^2 - 3$

So $g(3) = 3^2 - 3 = 9 - 3 = 6$

  $g(4) = 4^2 - 3 = 16 - 3 = 13.$

Similarly, if $h(x) \longrightarrow 4x - 5$,

  $h(9) \longrightarrow 4(9) - 5 = 31$

Sometimes we want the **inverse** function, which reverses the process.

If $h(x) = 4x - 5$, then $h^{-1}(x) = \frac{1}{4}(x + 5)$.

This symbol denotes 'inverse'

This is because $h(2)=4(2)-5=3$ and $h^{-1}(3)=\frac{1}{4}(3+5)=2$, reverses the process.

To find inverse functions, it is easy to substitute a dummy variable like this:

if $h(x)=4x-5$, let $y=4x-5$.

Now make x the subject, to get:

$$y+5=4x \implies x=\frac{1}{4}(y+5)$$

Finally, substitute y with x to get:

$$h^{-1}(x) = \frac{1}{4}(x+5).$$

So, variable 'y' has been used only to help with calculations.

Example

If $p(x) = 5x + 9$, find (a) $p^{-1}(x)$,   (b) $p^{-1}(8)$.

(a)   If $p(x) = 5x + 9$,

     let $y = 5x + 9 \implies x = \frac{y-9}{5}$.

     $\therefore p^{-1}(x) = \frac{x-9}{5}$.

(b)   Then $p^{-1}(8) = \frac{8-9}{5} = \frac{-1}{5}$.

Sometimes, we may want to combine functions.

If $f(x) = x^2 - 1$ and $g(x) = 2x + 3$, then clearly

$f(3) = 9 - 1 = 8$ and $g(-2) = -4 + 3 = -1$.

But suppose we want to take a number and first apply function f to it, and then apply function g to it – we write this as

| This is done second. | $\longrightarrow gf(x)$ | This is done first, so it is nearest to (x) |

So, for $gf(-1)$, we know that $f(x) = x^2 - 1 = (-1)^2 - 1 = 0$.

Then $g(0) = 2(0) + 3 = 3$.

So, $gf(-1) = 3$.

Example

If $p(x) = 2\sqrt{x-1}$ and $q(x) = 2x - 5$, then find:

(a) $q^{-1}(x)$, (b) $pq(5)$, (c) $qp(5)$.

(a)   Let $y = 2x - 5$, so $2x = y + 5$ and $x = \frac{1}{2}(y+5)$.

     Then, $q^{-1}(x) = \frac{1}{2}(x+5)$.

(b)   Now $q(5) = 2(5) - 5 = 5$ and $p(5) = 2\sqrt{5-1} = 2(2) = 4$.

     Hence, $pq(5) = 4$.

(c)   Now: $qp(5) = q(4) = 2(4) - 5 = 3$.

| As $p(5) = 2\sqrt{5-1} = 2(2)$ |

The square root of 4 could be +2 or −2, but we take the positive root only, unless told otherwise.

PROGRESS CHECK

1. If $f(x) = x^2 - 3$, $g(x) = 3x - 5$, $h(x) = 2x + 1$,
   find (a) g^{-1} (b) $gh(x)$ (c) $hg(x)$ (d) $hgf(2)$ (e) $gfh(1)$.

(a) $g^{-1}(x) = 1/3(x + 5)$ (b) $gh(x) = 6x - 2$ (c) $hg(x) = 6x - 9$ (d) $hgf(2) = -3$ (e) $gfh(1) = 13$

Graphical solutions

We have seen that simultaneous equations can be solved to find the points of intersection of graphs. So, if we draw the graphs of any given equations, their points of intersection will give the x and y values of their solution as simultaneous equations.

For example, Look at these graphs.

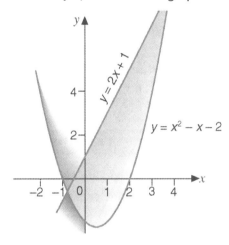

Read the values of x where the graphs meet.
$x = -0.8$, $x = 3.8$.
This time, do not substitute to find the corresponding values of y. The values of x are the roots of a quadratic equation. What is the equation?

$2x + 1 = x^2 - x - 2$ ⟵ | Substitute $2x+1$ for y. |

> You can check these using the formula.

$x^2 - 3x - 3 = 0$, which has roots -0.8 and 3.8, approximately.

| Rearranging |

Look again at this graph.

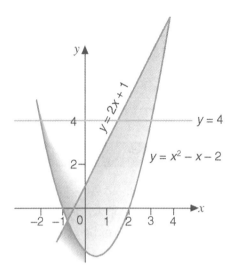

By drawing other straight lines, you can solve a range of equations.
Try $y = 0$ (the x-axis). The points of intersection will be the roots of $x^2 - x - 2 = 0$.
These are -1 and 2.
Try $y = 4$. The points of intersection will be the roots of $x^2 - x - 2 = 4$, or
$x^2 - x - 6 = 0$. These are -2 and 3.

Graphs of functions

There is a range of functions that you are expected to be able to graph. You
should also be able to recognise their characteristic shapes.

Here are some examples.

> The use of unknown
> constants, a, b, c,
> etc. may look
> complicated but in an
> examination they
> would be known
> numbers.

$y = ax^3 + bx^2 + cx + d$ (cubic); $\quad y = \dfrac{1}{x}$ (reciprocal);

$y = k^x$ (exponential); $y = \sin x$; $y = \cos x$.

Examples

(a) Draw the graph of $y = x^3 - x + 2$, from $x = -2$ to $x = 2$.

> Work out a table of values.

> You need to find
> the values at -0.5
> and 0.5 to find the
> right shape.

x	-2	-1	-0.5	0	0.5	1	2
y	-4	2	2.375	2	1.625	2	8

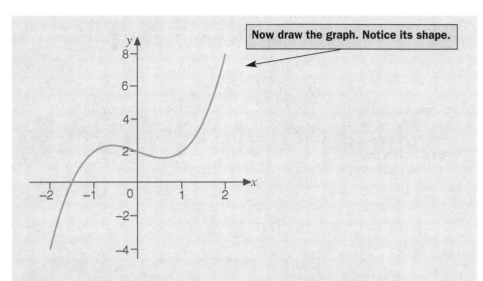

Now draw the graph. Notice its shape.

(b) Draw the graph of $y = \dfrac{2}{x}$ from $x = -4$ to $x = 4$, excluding 0.

Work out a table of values.

x	−4	−3	−2	−1	−0.5	0.5	1	2	3	4
y	−0.5	−0.67	−1	−2	−4	4	2	1	0.67	0.5

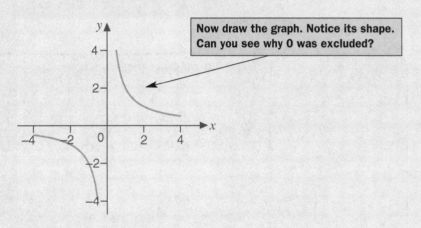

Now draw the graph. Notice its shape. Can you see why 0 was excluded?

(c) Draw the graph of $y = \sin x^{\circ}$ from $x = 0$ to $x = 360$.

Your calculator will work out the values for you.

There is no need to work out all the points as you can see that the negative values follow the positive ones.

Work out a table of values.

x	0	30	60	90	120	150	180	210	270	360
y	0	0.5	0.87	1	0.87	0.5	0	−0.5	−1	0

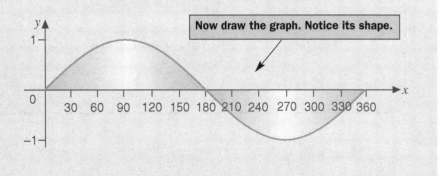

Now draw the graph. Notice its shape.

(d) Draw the graph of $y = 2^x$ from $x = -5$ to $x = 5$.

Work out a table of values.

Do not record too many figures in the table. You cannot plot 0.03125 that accurately!

x	−5	−4	−3	−2	−1	0	1	2	3	4	5
y	0.03	0.06	0.125	0.25	0.5	1	2	4	8	16	32

Now draw the graph. Notice its shape.

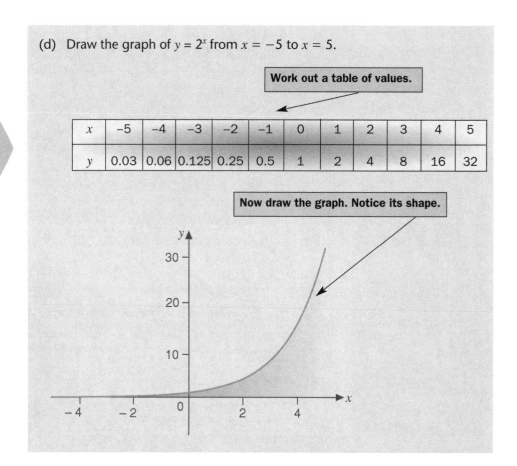

1 Draw the graphs of these functions.

(a) $y = x^3 + 2x - 1 = 0, \ -2 \leqslant x \leqslant 2$ (b) $y = \cos x^o, \ 0 \leqslant x \leqslant 360$

(c) $y = \dfrac{3}{x}, \ -3 \leqslant x < 0, \ 0 < x \leqslant 3$

2 Write down functions for which these could be the sketch graphs.

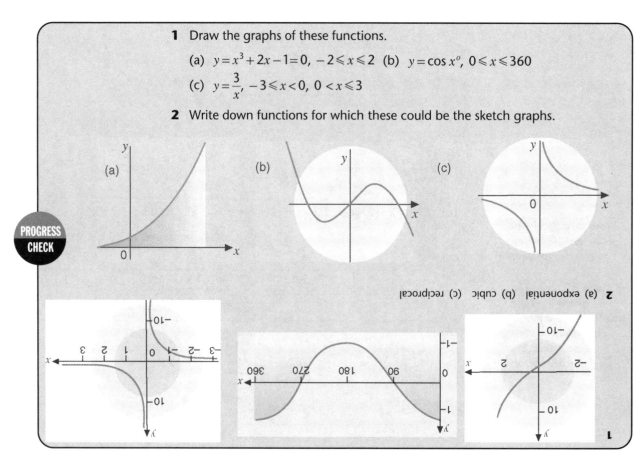

PROGRESS CHECK

2 (a) exponential (b) cubic (c) reciprocal

2.16 Transformation of functions

LEARNING SUMMARY

After studying this section, you will be able to:

● **apply transformations to the graphs of various functions**

Transforming graphs

The sketch graphs show the functions $y = f(x)$ and $y = f(x) + k$.

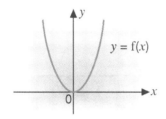

In relation to $y = f(x)$, where is the graph of $y = f(x) + k$, where k is a positive constant?

> **KEY POINT**
>
> For every value of x, y will be k more, that is the graph of $y = f(x)$ is translated by k in the y-direction, i.e., $\begin{pmatrix} 0 \\ k \end{pmatrix}$.

For example, the graph of $y = x^2 + 2$ is the graph of $y = x^2$ translated **2** units in the **y-direction**.

If in doubt, substitute a numerical value.

In relation to $y = f(x)$, where is the graph of $y = f(x + k)$, where k is a positive constant?

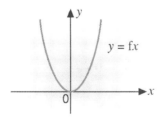

> **KEY POINT**
>
> For every value of x, y will take the value it would have had at $x + k$, that is the graph of $y = f(x)$ is translated by $-k$ in the x-direction, i.e., $\begin{pmatrix} -k \\ 0 \end{pmatrix}$.

For example, the graph of $y = \cos(x + 90)^0$ is the graph of $y = \cos x^0$ translated **90^0 to the left**.

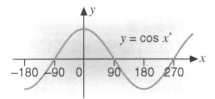

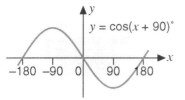

In relation to $y = f(x)$, where is the graph of $y = kf(x)$, where k is a positive constant?

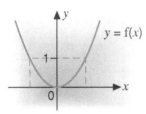

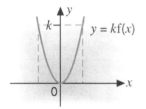

> **KEY POINT**
>
> For every value of x, y will be k times bigger, that is the graph of $y = f(x)$ is stretched by a factor of k in the y-direction.

For example, the graph of $y = 4x^3$ is the graph of $y = x^3$ stretched by a factor of **4** in the **y-direction**.

> The effect is similar to the previous transformation but it is not the same.

In relation to $y = f(x)$, where is the graph of $y = f(kx)$, where k is a positive constant?

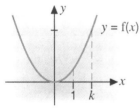

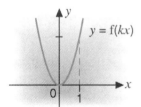

> **KEY POINT**
>
> For every value of x, y will take the value it would have had at kx, that is the graph of $y = f(x)$ is stretched by a factor $\dfrac{1}{k}$ in the x-direction.

For example, the graph of $y = \sin 2x$ is the graph of $y = \sin x$ stretched by factor $\frac{1}{2}$ (reduced by a factor 2) in the x-direction.

> All the graphs in this section are sketch graphs. You should show the correct shape and indicate where they cross the axes but they need not be accurate.

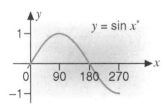

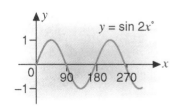

PROGRESS CHECK

1 Find the transformation in each case. Sketch the functions.
   (a) $y = x + 2$, $y = x - 2$ (b) $y = x^2$, $y = (x-3)^2$ (c) $y = \cos x$, $y = 2\cos x$
   (d) $y = \sin x^0$, $y = \sin(x - 180)^0$

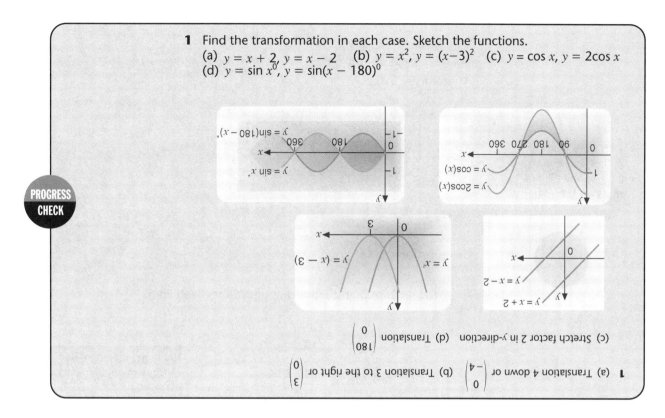

(c) Stretch factor 2 in y-direction   (d) Translation $\begin{pmatrix} 180 \\ 0 \end{pmatrix}$

1 (a) Translation 4 down or $\begin{pmatrix} 0 \\ -4 \end{pmatrix}$ (b) Translation 3 to the right or $\begin{pmatrix} 3 \\ 0 \end{pmatrix}$

2.17 Loci

LEARNING SUMMARY

After studying this section, you will be able to:
- **find loci involving straight lines and circles**
- **find the equations of circles**

Constructing loci

These are the loci you should be able to construct.

(a)   The locus of points equidistant from two fixed points A and B.

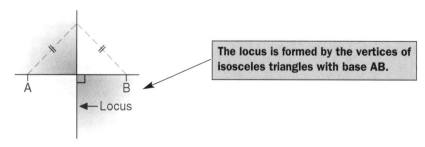

The locus is formed by the vertices of isosceles triangles with base AB.

'Loci' is a Latin word and is the plural of 'locus'.

 KEY POINT   The locus is the perpendicular bisector of the line AB.

Example

Draw the locus of points equidistant from (3, 2) and (7, 2).

What is its equation?

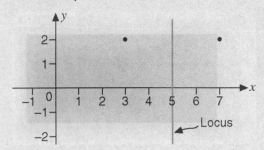

It is also the locus of points equidistant from (3, *y*) and (7, *y*), whatever the value of *y*.

The equation is $x = 5$.

(b)   The locus of points equidistant from two fixed lines.

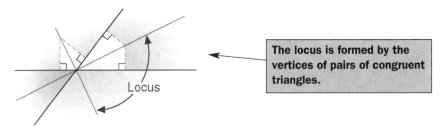

The locus is formed by the vertices of pairs of congruent triangles.

KEY POINT   **The locus is the bisectors of the angles between the two lines.**

Example

Draw the locus of points equidistant from both axes.

What is its equation?

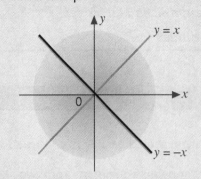

The equations are $y = x$ and $y = -x$.

Graphs of circles

There was some work on this in Section 2.10.

KEY POINT   **A circle is the locus of points at a fixed distance from a fixed point.**

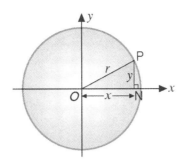

The radius of the circle is r, which is constant for a given circle.
Let the coordinates of a point P on the circle be (x, y).

$x^2 + y^2 = r^2$

> Apply Pythagoras' theorem to triangle OPN.

As P is any point on the circle, the relationship is true for all points on the circle and is therefore its equation.

> **KEY POINT**
> The equation of a circle, centre the origin and radius r, is $x^2 + y^2 = r^2$.

Example
Find the locus of points which are equidistant from the axes and 5 units from the origin.

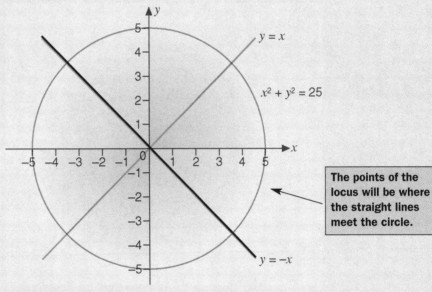

The points of the locus will be where the straight lines meet the circle.

The first two are the angle bisectors found earlier.

The equations are $y = x$, $y = -x$ and $x^2 + y^2 = 25$.

Find the intersection of $y = x$ and $x^2 + y^2 = 25$.
Substitute x for y.

$x^2 + x^2 = 25$
$2x^2 = 25$
$x^2 = 12.5$
$x = \pm\sqrt{12.5} = \pm 3.54$

> Since $y = x$, the values of y are also ± 3.54.

Remember that the pairs of values go together in the same order, positive with positive and negative with negative.

Find the intersection of $y = -x$ and $x^2 + y^2 = 25$.
Substitute x for y.

Since $(-x)^2 = x^2$

$x^2 + x^2 = 25$

$2x^2 = 25$

$x^2 = 12.5$

$x = \pm\sqrt{12.5} = 3.54 \text{ or } -3.54$

Since $y = x$, the values of y are now -3.54 or 3.54.

Remember that the pairs of values go together in the same order, positive with negative and negative with positive.

The locus is four points (3.54, 3.54), (3.54, −3.54), (−3.54, 3.54), (−3.54, −3.54).

PROGRESS CHECK

1 Find the equations of these loci.
   (a) Points equidistant from (1, 1) and (1, 7)
   (b) Circle centre O and radius 6
2 Find all the points that are 6 units from O and equidistant from (1, 1) and (1, 7).

1 (a) $y = 4$ (b) $x^2 + y^2 = 36$ 2 (4.47, 4), (−4.47, 4)

Sample IGCSE questions

1 (a) Expand the brackets and simplify the expressions.
  (i) $3x\,(x-3)-4\,(3x-2)$
  (ii) $(2x+3)(x-2)$ **[5]**

(b) Factorise these expressions.
  (i) $4xy^2-2x^2\,y$
  (ii) $x^2-3x-28$ **[4]**

(c) Simplify these expressions.
  (i) $(3xy^3)^2$
  (ii) $\dfrac{2a^{-2}b^3}{4ab^{-1}}$ **[4]**

Expand the brackets, remembering that $-4\times-2=8$

Collect like terms.

Expand the brackets. Collect like terms.

The common factor is $2xy$.

Find two numbers with sum -3 and product -28.

Remember that $(y^3)^2=y^{3\times2}=y^6$

Either form is acceptable.

(a) (i) $3x^2-9x-12x+8$ ✔✔

  $3x^2-21x+8$ ✔

  (ii) $2x^2+3x-4x-6$ ✔

  $2x^2-x-6$ ✔

(b) (i) $2xy\,(2y-x)$ ✔✔

  (ii) $(x-7)(x+4)$ ✔✔

(c) (i) $9x^2y^6$ ✔✔

  (ii) $\dfrac{1}{2}a^{-3}b^4$ or $\dfrac{b^4}{2a^3}$ ✔✔

2 An aircraft flew across the Atlantic, a distance of 3000 miles. On the return flight, the average speed was 100 miles per hour faster.
The total journey time was 10 hours.
What was the average speed on the first part of the journey? **[10]**

This is an example of a multi-step question. You have to decide on your method and how to start the question.

Remember that time is distance divided by speed.

Multiply each side by $x\,(x+100)$.

Expand the brackets and collect terms.

Let the average speed on the first part be x mph.

Time for the first part $=\dfrac{3000}{x}$ ✔

Time for second part $=\dfrac{3000}{x+100}$ ✔

Total time is 10 hours, giving equation

$=\dfrac{3000}{x}+\dfrac{3000}{x+100}=10$ ✔

$3000(x+100)+3000x=10x\,(x+100)$ ✔

Sample IGCSE questions

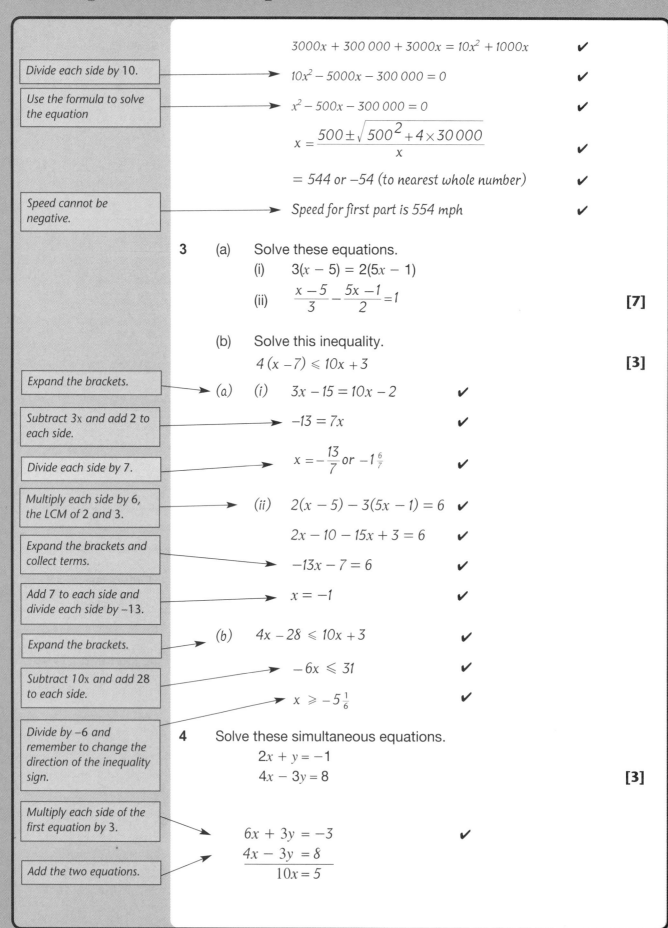

$$3000x + 300\,000 + 3000x = 10x^2 + 1000x \quad ✔$$

Divide each side by 10.

$$10x^2 - 5000x - 300\,000 = 0 \quad ✔$$

Use the formula to solve the equation

$$x^2 - 500x - 300\,000 = 0 \quad ✔$$

$$x = \frac{500 \pm \sqrt{500^2 + 4 \times 30\,000}}{x} \quad ✔$$

$$= 544 \text{ or } -54 \text{ (to nearest whole number)} \quad ✔$$

Speed cannot be negative.

Speed for first part is 554 mph ✔

3 (a) Solve these equations.

  (i) $3(x - 5) = 2(5x - 1)$

  (ii) $\dfrac{x - 5}{3} - \dfrac{5x - 1}{2} = 1$ **[7]**

  (b) Solve this inequality.

  $4(x - 7) \leqslant 10x + 3$ **[3]**

Expand the brackets.

(a) (i) $3x - 15 = 10x - 2$ ✔

Subtract 3x and add 2 to each side.

$-13 = 7x$ ✔

Divide each side by 7.

$x = -\dfrac{13}{7} \text{ or } -1\frac{6}{7}$ ✔

Multiply each side by 6, the LCM of 2 and 3.

(ii) $2(x - 5) - 3(5x - 1) = 6$ ✔

$2x - 10 - 15x + 3 = 6$ ✔

Expand the brackets and collect terms.

$-13x - 7 = 6$ ✔

Add 7 to each side and divide each side by −13.

$x = -1$ ✔

Expand the brackets.

(b) $4x - 28 \leqslant 10x + 3$ ✔

Subtract 10x and add 28 to each side.

$-6x \leqslant 31$ ✔

$x \geqslant -5\frac{1}{6}$ ✔

Divide by −6 and remember to change the direction of the inequality sign.

4 Solve these simultaneous equations.

$2x + y = -1$

$4x - 3y = 8$ **[3]**

Multiply each side of the first equation by 3.

$6x + 3y = -3$ ✔

$\underline{4x - 3y = 8}$

Add the two equations.

$10x = 5$

Sample IGCSE questions

$$x = \tfrac{1}{2}$$ ✔

Substitute for x in the first equation. → $2 \times \tfrac{1}{2} + y = -1$

$$y = -2$$ ✔

5 This formula is used in physics.

Notice that v occurs twice in the formula. → $f = \dfrac{uv}{u + v}$

Make v the subject of the formula. **[5]**

Multiply each side by $(u + v)$. → $f(u + v) = uv$ ✔

Expand the brackets. → $uf + vf = uv$ ✔

Change the sides over and subtract vf from each side. → $uv - vf = uf$ ✔

$v(u - f) = uf$ ✔

Factorise and divide each side by $(u - f)$. → $v = \dfrac{uf}{u - f}$ ✔

6 (a) Draw the graph of $y = x^3 + 2x^2$ for $-3 \leqslant x \leqslant 2$. **[4]**

(b) Use your graph to solve $x^3 + 2x^2 = 4$. **[2]**

(c) Use trial and improvement to find this solution correct to two decimal places. **[4]**

(a)

x	-3	-2	-1.5	-1	-0.5	0	0.5	1	2
y	-9	0	1.125	1	0.375	0	0.625	3	16

✔✔

Find some values between the integer points to help draw the curve.

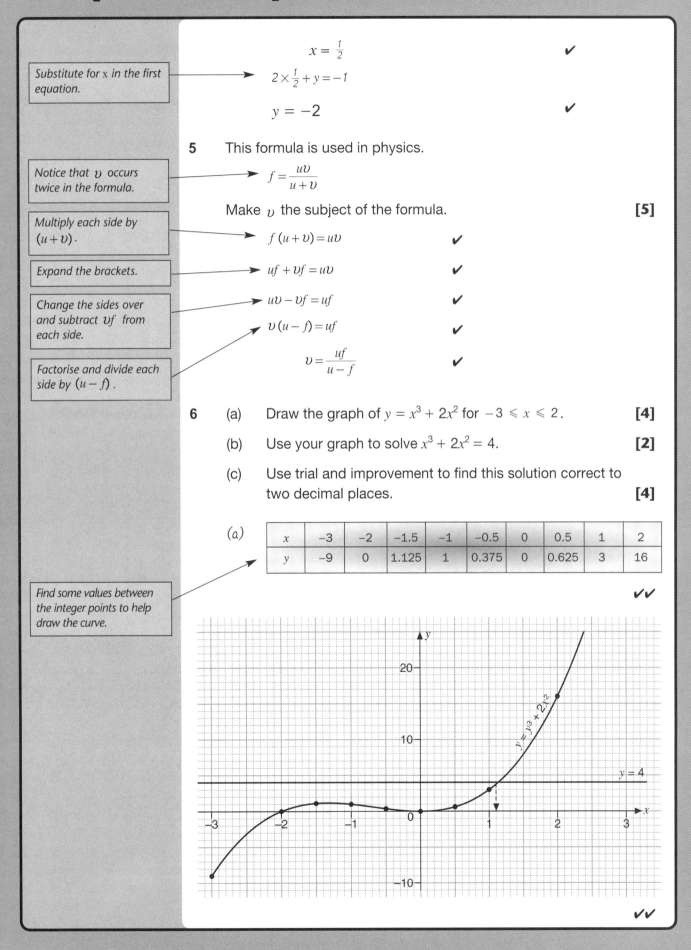

✔✔

Sample IGCSE questions

Substituting $y =$ in the equation of the graph gives the required equation.

(b)   Draw the line $y = 4$. ✔
      Read the graph, $x = 1.1$ ✔

You may have read this as 1.2. This is acceptable.

(c) $x = 1.2$, $x^3 + 2x^2 = 4.608$

      $x = 1.1$, $x^3 + 2x^2 = 3.751$ ✔

Too high, so the root is between 1.1 and 1.15.

      $x = 1.15$, $x^3 + 2x^2 = 4.16 ...$ ✔

This is very close, but too low.

      $x = 1.13$, $x^3 + 2x^2 = 3.996 ...$ ✔

This shows that the root is between 1.13 and 1.135 and is therefore 1.13 to 2 d.p.

      $x = 1.135$, $x^3 + 2x^2 = 4.0385 ...$ ✔

      Solution $x = 1.13$

The last mark is awarded only if the reason for selecting 1.13 is shown.

7 (a) Find the gradient of the straight line $2x + 5y = 15$. **[2]**

    (b) Find the equations of the straight lines through (0, 2) that are parallel and perpendicular to the line in part (a). **[4]**

Rearrange in the form $y = mx + c$.

    (a) $5y = 15 - 2x$

         $y = 3 - \dfrac{2}{5}x$ ✔

         Gradient $-\dfrac{2}{5}$ ✔

There is 1 mark for the gradient and 1 for the intercept.

    (b) Parallel line: $y = 2 - \dfrac{2}{5}x$ or $5y = 10 - 2x$ ✔✔

         Perpendicular line: $y = 2 + \dfrac{5}{2}x$ or $2y = 5x + 4$ ✔✔

8 The sketch shows the graph of $y = f(x)$.

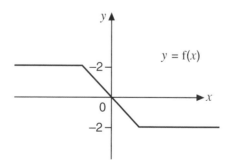

Sample IGCSE questions

Draw sketches to show the graphs of

(a) $y = f(x) + 3$ (b) $y = f(x + 2)$ (c) $y = \frac{1}{2} f(x)$ **[5]**

In (a) the translation is $\begin{pmatrix} 0 \\ 3 \end{pmatrix}$, in (b) $\begin{pmatrix} -2 \\ 0 \end{pmatrix}$ and in (c) there is a stretch (reduction) of factor $\frac{1}{2}$. You should show this by marking the axes.

(a)

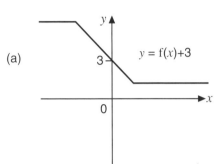

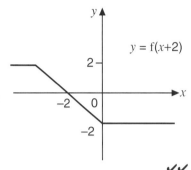

(c)

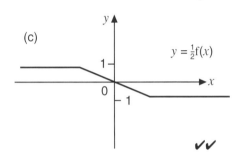

Exam practice questions

1 (a) Solve these equations.
  (i) $3(2 - x) = 2(x - 6)$
  (ii) $\dfrac{x}{2} - \dfrac{x-1}{3} = 1$ **[5]**

(b) Solve these inequalities.
  (i) $4x \leqslant 3(2x - 3)$
  (ii) $x^2 \leqslant 225$ **[6]**

2 (a) Make v the subject of the formula $\dfrac{1}{u} - \dfrac{1}{v} = \dfrac{1}{f}$. **[3]**

(b) Make q the subject of the formula $p = \dfrac{qr}{r - q}$. **[4]**

3 Mark and Brian ordered cups of coffee and biscuits from a buffet bar.
Mark bought 2 cups of coffee and 3 biscuits. They cost $3.23.
Brian bought 3 cups of coffee and 1 biscuit. They cost $2.92.
Write down two simultaneous equations and solve them to find the cost of a cup of coffee
and the cost of a biscuit. **[5]**

4 (a) Draw the graph of $y = x^3 + 2x^2 + 1$ between $x = -1$ and $x = 3$. **[3]**
(b) Use your graph to solve these equations.
  (i) $x^3 - 2x^2 + 1 = 0$
  (ii) $x^3 - 2x^2 + 1 = 5$ **[3]**
(c) Use trial and improvement to find the solution of $x^3 - 2x^2 - 4 = 0$, correct to two
decimal places. **[4]**

5 Find the points of intersection of the straight line $2x + y = 3$ with the circle $x^2 + y^2 = 16$. **[7]**

6 (a) Factorise $x^2 - 2x - 15$. **[2]**
(b) Solve the equation $x^2 - 2x - 15 = 0$. **[1]**
(c) Solve the inequality $x^2 - 2x - 15 > 0$. **[4]**

7 The sketch shows the graph of $y = f(x)$.

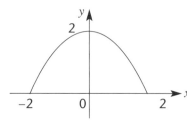

Sketch the graphs of

(a) $y = f(x) + 1$ **[1]**
(b) $y = f(x - 2)$ **[1]**
(c) $y = \dfrac{1}{2} f(x)$ **[1]**

Overview

Topic	Section	Studied in class	Revised	Practice questions
3.1 Congruent triangles	Tests for congruency			
3.2 Properties of triangles and quadrilaterals	Sum of angles of a triangle			
	Properties of quadrilaterals			
3.3 Right-angled triangles	Pythagoras' theorem			
	The length of the line joining two points on a graph			
	Problems in three dimensions			
3.4 Trigonometry	Trigonometric ratios			
	Area of a triangle			
	Sine, cosine and tangent of any angle			
	Sine and cosine rules			
3.5 Angles in lines and polygons	Angles			
	Polygons			
3.6 Circles	Cyclic quadrilaterals			
	Angle theorems			
	Chord theorems			
	Tangents			
3.7 3-D shapes	Cylinders			
	Prisms and other shapes			
3.8 Transformations	Reflections and translations			
	Rotations			
	Enlargements			
3.9 Matrices	Operations on matrices			
	Determinant			
3.10 Area and volume	Dimensions			
	Areas and volumes of similar figures			
3.11 Vectors	Zero vector and unit vectors			
	Inverse vectors			
	Vector addition and subtraction			
	Magnitude of vectors			
3.12 Measures and constructions	Upper and lower bounds			
	Compound units			
	Constructions			
3.13 Mensuration	The sphere			
	Arcs, sectors and segments			
3.14 Loci	Three important loci			

3.1 Congruent triangles

LEARNING SUMMARY

After studying this section, you will be able to:

● apply the tests for congruent triangles

Tests for congruency

 KEY POINT If two triangles are **congruent** they must have the same shape and the same size. This means that they will fit exactly onto each other when one of them is rotated, reflected or translated.

Two triangles are congruent if any of these conditions are satisfied:

● two sides and the included angle of one triangle are equal to the two sides and the included angle of the other triangle (side, angle, side or SAS)

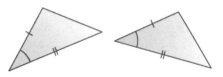

● the three sides of one triangle are equal to the corresponding three sides of the other triangle (side, side, side or SSS)

● two angles and a side in one triangle are equal to two angles and the corresponding side in the other triangle (angle, corresponding angle side or AAS)

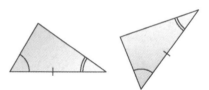

● each triangle is right-angled and the hypotenuse and one side of one triangle is equal to the hypotenuse and a side of the other triangle, (right angle, hypotenuse, side or RHS).

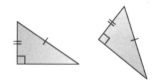

The hypotenuse is the side opposite the right angle.

The tests for congruency: SSS; SAS; ASA are essentially the methods used to construct triangles (note that construction is discussed further in section 3.12):

(a) SSS
  (i)   Draw the line AB of given length.
  (ii) Use compasses to construct arcs AC and BC.
  (iii) Draw AC and BC.

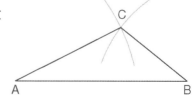

The test involving two sides and an angle is valid only if the angle is the included angle. If the given angle is not the included angle then there are two possible solutions: the ambiguous case.

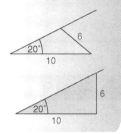

(b) SAS

   (i)   Draw a line AB of given length.

   (ii) Measure and draw the angle at A.

   (iii) Draw the line AC of given length.

   (iv) Join C to B.

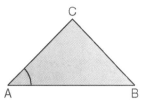

(c) ASA

   (i)   Draw the line AB of given length.

   (ii) Measure and draw the angles at A and B.

   (iii) Draw lines AC and BC.

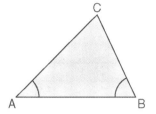

The basic checks for congruency are:

(a) the three sides of each triangle are equal

(b) two sides and the included angle in each triangle are equal

(c) two angles and the corresponding side in each triangle are equal

(d) for a right-angled triangle the check is 'right angle, hypotenuse and side' in each triangle are equal.

When looking for equal angles, you need to remember the angle facts for parallel lines.

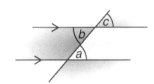

angle a = angle b (alternate angles)

angle a = angle c (corresponding angles)

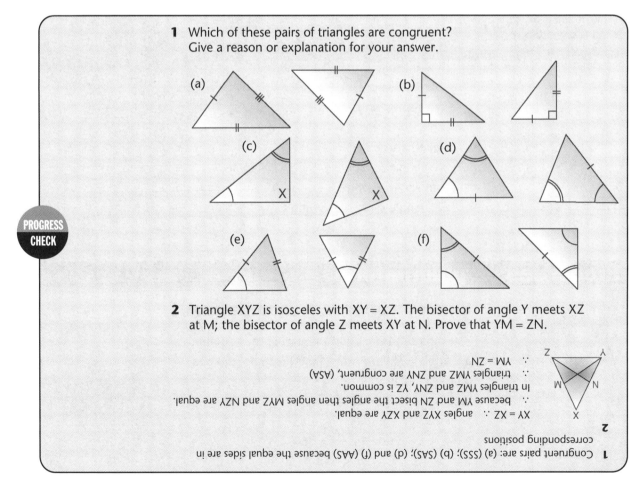

PROGRESS CHECK

1 Which of these pairs of triangles are congruent? Give a reason or explanation for your answer.

(a)   (b)

(c)   (d)

(e)   (f)

2 Triangle XYZ is isosceles with XY = XZ. The bisector of angle Y meets XZ at M; the bisector of angle Z meets XY at N. Prove that YM = ZN.

1 Congruent pairs are: (a) (SSS); (b) (SAS); (d) and (f) (AAS) because the equal sides are in corresponding positions

2

XY = XZ ∴ angles XYZ and XZY are equal.

∴ because YM and ZN bisect the angles then angles MYZ and NZY are equal.

In triangles YMZ and ZNY, YZ is common.

∴ triangles YMZ and ZNY are congruent, (ASA)

∴ YM = ZN

Shape and Space

3.2 Properties of triangles and quadrilaterals

LEARNING SUMMARY

After studying this section, you will be able to:

- **use the angle sum of a triangle and a quadrilateral**
- **identify quadrilaterals by their geometric properties**

Sum of angles of a triangle

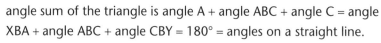

You need to be able to prove that:

(a) the sum of the angles in a triangle is 180°.

Take any triangle ABC. Construct XY through B and parallel to AC. Using the properties of parallel lines, angle A = angle XBA and angle C = angle CBY. Hence the

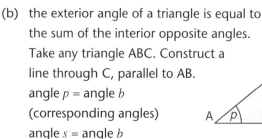

> You must remember the basic angle facts such as the sum of the angles on a straight line is 180°, and the properties of alternate and corresponding angles.

angle sum of the triangle is angle A + angle ABC + angle C = angle XBA + angle ABC + angle CBY = 180° = angles on a straight line.

(b) the exterior angle of a triangle is equal to the sum of the interior opposite angles.

Take any triangle ABC. Construct a line through C, parallel to AB.

angle p = angle b
(corresponding angles)

angle s = angle b
(alternate angles)

∴   angle p + angle s = angle a + angle b

but angle r = angle a + angle b

∴   angle p + angle s = angle r

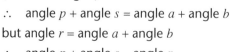

Properties of quadrilaterals

Sum of angles in a quadrilateral

You can use the fact that the sum of the angles in a triangle = 180° to prove that the angle sum of a quadrilateral is 360°.

angles $a + b + c = 180°$

angles $d + e + f = 180°$

∴ $a + b + c + d + e + f = 360°$

Geometric properties of quadrilaterals

You need to be able to identify quadrilaterals by their geometric properties.

Make sure you remember these properties

(a) Square

- all sides equal and opposite sides parallel
- all angles 90°
- four lines of symmetry
- rotational symmetry order 4
- diagonals bisect at right angles

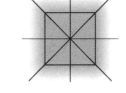

(b) Rectangle

- opposite sides equal and parallel
- all angles 90°
- two lines of symmetry
- rotational symmetry order 2

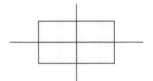

(c) Parallelogram

- opposite sides equal and parallel
- opposite angles equal
- no lines of symmetry
- rotational symmetry order 2

(d) Rhombus

- all sides equal
- opposite sides parallel
- two lines of symmetry
- rotational symmetry order 2
- diagonals bisect at right angles

(e) Kite

- one line of symmetry
- diagonals intersect at right angles
- two pairs of adjacent sides equal

(f) Trapezium

- one pair of sides parallel

Note: isosceles trapezium has one line of symmetry

Examples

Find the size of the angles marked with letters:

(a)

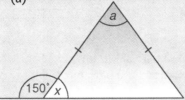

(b)

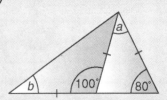

(a) Angle $x = 30°$ (angles on a straight line)

Angle $a = 180° - 30° - 30° = 120°$ (angle sum of isosceles triangle)

(b) Angle $b = (180° - 100°) \div 2 = 40°$ (angle sum of isosceles triangle)

Angle $c = 180° - 80° - 80° = 20°$ (angle sum of isosceles triangle)

PROGRESS CHECK

1 Find the size of the angles marked with letters:

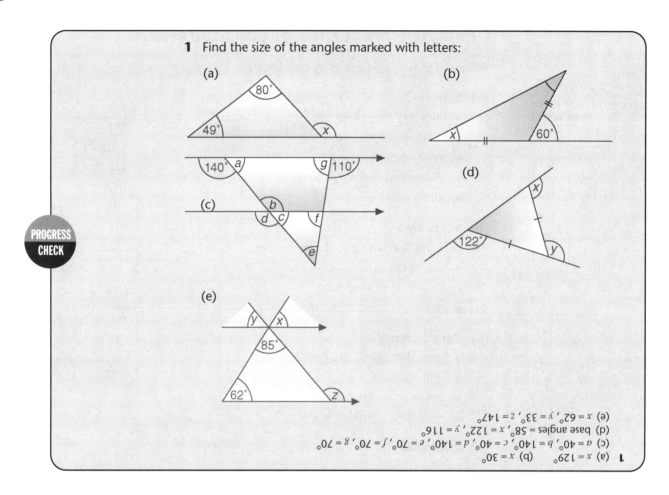

(a)

(b)

(c)

(d)

(e)

1 (a) $x = 129°$ (b) $x = 30°$
(c) $a = 40°$, $b = 140°$, $c = 40°$, $d = 140°$, $e = 70°$, $f = 70°$, $g = 70°$
(d) base angles $= 58°$, $x = 122°$, $y = 116°$
(e) $x = 62°$, $y = 33°$, $z = 147°$

3.3 Right-angled triangles

LEARNING SUMMARY

After studying this section, you will be able to:

- **find the third side in a right-angled triangle**
- **find the length of a line joining two points on a graph**
- **use Pythagoras' theorem to solve problems in three dimensions**

Pythagoras' theorem

KEY POINT

Pythagoras' theorem can be stated as:

In a right-angled triangle, the area of the square on the hypotenuse = the sum of the areas of the squares on the other two sides.

but it is normally abbreviated to:

The square on the hypotenuse = the sum of the squares on the other two sides.

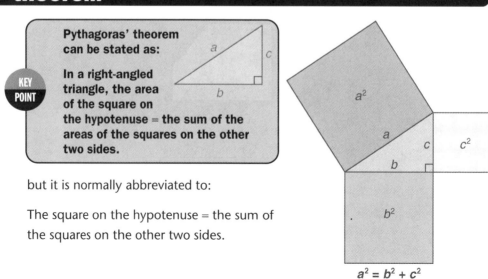

$$a^2 = b^2 + c^2$$

Examples

Find the missing side in each of these triangles:

> Always label the sides of the triangle, a, b, c, and then substitute in the formula before rearranging.

(a)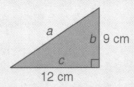

a b | 9 cm c 12 cm

(b)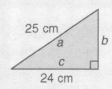

25 cm a b c 24 cm

> It is a good idea to draw a sketch if a diagram isn't given. Try to draw it roughly to scale and mark on it any lengths you know. It may help you see any errors in your working.

(a)
$$a^2 = b^2 + c^2$$
$$a^2 = 9^2 + 12^2$$
$$= 81 + 144$$
$$= 225$$
$$a = \sqrt{225}$$
$$= 15 \text{ cm}$$

(b)
$$a^2 = b^2 + c^2$$
$$25^2 = b^2 + 24^2$$
$$625 = b^2 + 576$$
$$b^2 = 625 - 576$$
$$b = \sqrt{49}$$
$$= 7 \text{ cm}$$

KEY POINT   Learn Pythagoras' theorem: $a^2 = b^2 + c^2$

The length of the line joining two points on a graph

You can calculate the length of the line joining two points using Pythagoras' theorem.

Example

In the diagram A is at $(5, 5)$ and B is at $(18, 20)$.
Find the length AB.

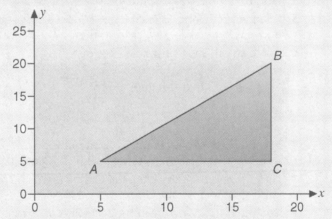

Find the lengths of AC and BC from the coordinates of A and B.

AC is the difference between the x-coordinates = 13

BC is the difference between the y-coordinates = 15

$$AB^2 = AC^2 + BC^2$$
$$= 13^2 + 15^2$$
$$= 169 + 225$$
$$= 394$$
$$AB = \sqrt{394}$$
$$= 19.8 \text{ to 3 s.f.}$$

Problems in three dimensions

Example

The diagram shows a cuboid 5 cm by 4 cm by 12 cm.

Find the lengths of AC and AG.

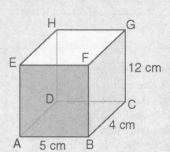

In triangle ABC:
$$AC^2 = 5^2 + 4^2$$
$$= 25 + 16$$
$$= 41$$
$$AC = 6.4 \text{ cm}$$

In triangle ACG:
$$AG^2 = AC^2 + CG^2$$
$$= 41 + 144$$
$$= 185$$
$$AG = 13.6 \text{ cm}$$

PROGRESS CHECK

1 Find the missing side in each triangle:

(a) 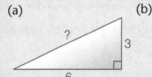 (b) 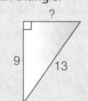 (c)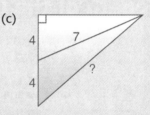

2 A rectangular field has a length of 250 m and a width of 130 m. Find the length of the diagonal path across it.

3 A ladder, 6 m long, is resting against a wall. If the top of the ladder is 4 m above the ground, how far from the wall is the base of the ladder?

4 The diagram shows the side view of a shed.

Find the length of the sloping roof.

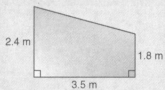

5 The diagonal of a rectangle is 2 cm longer than the length. If the width of the rectangle is 10 cm find the length.

6 Find the length of the diagonal of a rectangular room of length 4.8 m, width 3 m and height 2.6 m.

7 Find the distance between the following pairs of points:

(a) A(3, 4) and B(10, 6)   (b) A(4, 5) and B(−3, −8)

8 ABCD is a rectangular display area. AM is a vertical mast at the corner of the area. The top of the mast, M, is connected by straight supporting wires to the corners B, C and D.

Calculate the height of the mast, AM, and the lengths of the wires, BM and CM.

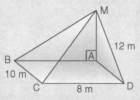

8 AM = 6.6 m, BM = 10.4 m, CM = 14.4 m
7 (a) 7.28 (b) 14.76
6 6.2 m
5 $(x + 2)^2 = x^2 + 10^2$ ∴ $x^2 + 4x + 4 = x^2 + 100$
  $4x = 96$, ∴ $x = 24$ cm
4 3.6 m
1 (a) 6.7 (b) 9.4 (c) 9.8   2 281.8 m   3 4.5 m

3.4 Trigonometry

LEARNING SUMMARY

After studying this section, you will be able to:

- use the sine, cosine and tangent ratios to find angles and sides in right-angled triangles
- find the area of a triangle using the formula $A = \frac{1}{2}\,ab\,\sin C$
- find the sine, cosine and tangent of any angle
- use the sine and cosine rules

Trigonometric ratios

You can use Pythagoras' theorem to solve problems in three dimensions: In a right-angled triangle the sides and the angles are related by three trigonometrical ratios: the sine (abbreviated to sin), the cosine (abbreviated to cos) and the tangent (abbreviated to tan).

To use these remember that you need to identify which side is the hypotenuse (the longest side), which is the opposite (opposite the given angle), and which is the adjacent (next to the given angle), thus:

Label the sides hypotenuse, opposite and adjacent.

KEY POINT

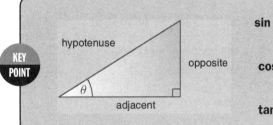

$$\sin \theta = \frac{\text{opposite}}{\text{hypotenuse}},$$

$$\cos \theta = \frac{\text{adjacent}}{\text{hypotenuse}},$$

$$\tan \theta = \frac{\text{opposite}}{\text{adjacent}}$$

You must remember these three ratios.

Examples

(a) Find the length, to 2d.p., of the side marked x in this triangle.

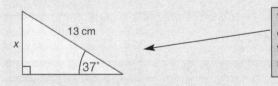

You have been given the length of the hypotenuse and need to find the opposite side, so you need to use the sine.

$\sin 37 = \dfrac{x}{13}$ thus $x = 13 \times \sin 37$

$\quad = 13 \times 0.6018 = 7.8235 = 7.82$ cm to 2d.p.

(b) Find the angle θ in this triangle:

6.5 cm

14.3 cm

> You are given the lengths of the opposite and adjacent so you need to use the tangent.

$$\tan \theta = \frac{\text{opposite}}{\text{hypotenuse}}$$

$$= = \frac{14.3}{6.5}$$

$$= 2.2$$

$$\therefore \quad \theta = \tan^{-1} 2.2$$

$$= 65.6°$$

> The 'tan^{-1}' shows that we need the angle whose tangent is 2.2.

(c) ABCD is a rectangular field. AM is a vertical pole at the corner A. BC = 5 m, CD = 10 m and the angle of elevation of M from B is 25°.

Calculate
(i)   the height of the pole AM
(ii) the angle of elevation of M from C.

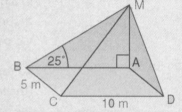

(i)   AM = AB tan 25
$$= 10 \times 0.4663$$
$$= 4.66 \text{ m}$$

(ii) $AC^2 = AD^2 + CD^2$
$$= 25 + 100$$
$$AC = \sqrt{125} = 11.18 \text{ m}$$

$$\text{Tangent of angle MCA} = \frac{AM}{AC}$$

$$= = \frac{4.66}{11.18}$$

$$\therefore \qquad \text{Angle MCA} = \tan^{-1} 0.4168$$

$$= 22.6°$$

Area of a triangle

You can calculate the area of a triangle using the sine of an angle.
The formula is:

> **KEY POINT**
>
> **Area** $= \frac{1}{2}ab \sin C$, **or** $= \frac{1}{2}bc \sin A$, **or** $= \frac{1}{2}ac \sin B$

Example
Find the area of this triangle.

$$\text{Area} = = \frac{1}{2}ab \sin C$$

$$= = \frac{1}{2} \times 14 \times 12 \times \sin 65$$

$$= 76.13 \text{ cm}^2$$

A

12 cm

c   b

65°

C

B   a   14 cm

Sine, cosine and tangent of any angle

You already know that, in a right-angled triangle, the sine, cosine and tangent are defined as:

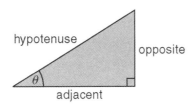

$$\sin \theta = \frac{\text{opposite}}{\text{hypotenuse}},$$

$$\cos \theta = \frac{\text{adjacent}}{\text{hypotenuse}},$$

$$\tan \theta = \frac{\text{opposite}}{\text{adjacent}}$$

You should also know that it is possible to define the trigonometric ratios for angles of any size using coordinates.

Draw a circle with radius 1 unit. The point P with coordinates (x, y) moves round the circumference of the circle.

OP makes an angle θ with the positive x-axis. The angle increases as P rotates anticlockwise.

For any angle θ, the sine, cosine and tangent are given by the coordinates of P.

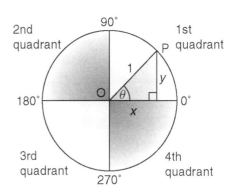

$$\sin \theta = = \frac{y}{1} = y, \ \cos \theta = = \frac{x}{1} = x, \ \tan \theta = = \frac{y}{x}$$

Notice that as P rotates, the coordinates change sign.
In the first quadrant, from 0° to 90° both y and x are positive.
In the second quadrant, from 90° to 180° y is positive but x is negative.
In the third quadrant, from 180° to 270° both y and x are negative.
In the fourth quadrant, from 270° to 360° y is negative but x is positive.
Thus the sign of the sine, cosine and tangent of an angle changes according to

After 360° the pattern continues: the sine, cosine and tangent taking the appropriate sign according to the quadrant.

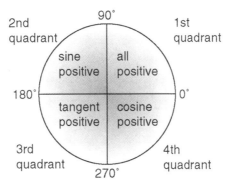

the size of the angle, that is the sign depends on which quadrant the angle is in.

The graphs of the three ratios, sine, cosine and tangent are shown on page 116 in Figures 1, 2 and 3. You need to recognise them and distinguish between them.

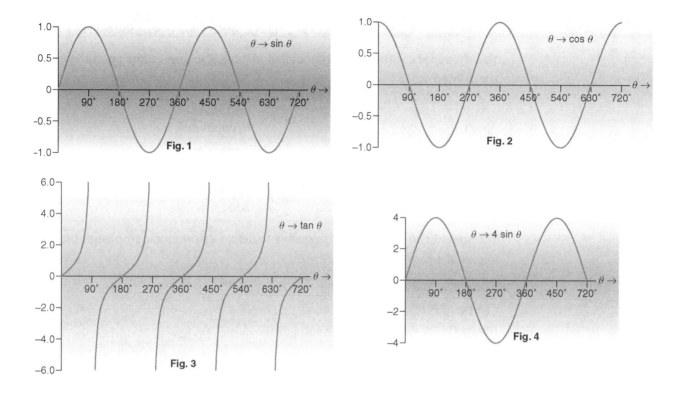

The sine curve models many natural phenomena including sound and light waves. Because it repeats every 360° the graph is described as periodic with period 360°. (The other curves are similarly periodic with periods 360° for the cosine and 180° for the tangent.) Note that the tangent curve is of a different form and at 90°, 270°, 450° etc. the value of the tangent is infinity and hence cannot be plotted.

The graph of $\sin \theta$ oscillates between −1 and +1. This means that the amplitude of the sine curve is 1. The amplitude can be changed by multiplying $\sin \theta$ by a number, for example 4. The graph of $4 \sin \theta$ is shown in Figure 4.

You can use graphs like these to solve equations involving trigonometrical functions.

Example

Draw the graphs of $y = 6 \sin x$ and $y = 4$. Use these graphs to solve the equation $3 \sin x = 2$ for $0° \leqslant x \leqslant 360°$.

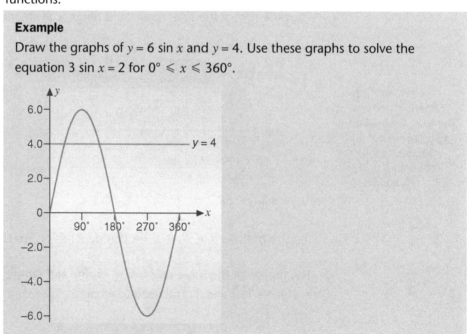

At the point where the graphs intersect $6 \sin x = 4$.

Dividing by 2 gives $3 \sin x = 2$.

The graphs intersect at approximately 40° and 135°.

(using a calculator gives 41.8° and 138.2°)

Sine and cosine rules

The sine and cosine rules apply to all triangles.

The sine rule

The sine rule is used to find the missing sides and angles in a triangle if: (a) the length of one side and the sizes of two angles are known, or (b) the lengths of two sides and the size of the angle opposite to one of those two sides are known.

Remember that angles are shown with capital letters and sides with lower case letters.

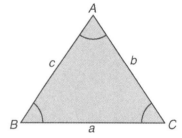

KEY POINT

The sine rule:

$$\frac{a}{\sin A} = \frac{b}{\sin B} = \frac{c}{\sin c} \quad \text{or} \quad \frac{\sin A}{a} = \frac{\sin B}{b} = \frac{\sin C}{c}$$

Examples

(a) In triangle *ABC*, find the missing sides and angle.

From the sine rule:

$$\frac{a}{\sin A} = \frac{b}{\sin B} = \frac{c}{\sin C}$$

$$\frac{9.5}{\sin 55} = \frac{c}{\sin 60}$$

$$c = \frac{9.5 \times \sin 65}{\sin 55} = 10.5 \text{ cm}$$

Angle $B = 180° - 65° - 55° = 60°$

$$\frac{9.5}{\sin 55} = \frac{b}{\sin 60}$$

$$b = \frac{9.5 \times \sin 60}{\sin 55} = 10.0 \text{ cm}$$

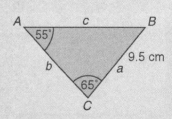

(b) Find the size of angle A in this triangle.

$$\frac{\sin A}{a}=\frac{\sin C}{c}$$

$$\frac{\sin A}{7}=\frac{\sin 40}{12}$$

$$\sin A=\frac{7\times\sin 40}{12}=0.375$$

$$\therefore\quad A=\sin^{-1}0.375$$

$$=22°$$

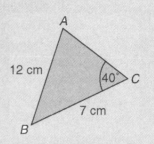

The cosine rule

> **KEY POINT**
>
> **The cosine rule:**
> $a^2=b^2+c^2-2bc\cos A$
>
> or $b^2=c^2+a^2-2ca\cos B$;
> or $c^2=a^2+b^2-2ab\cos C$

There are two ways of using the cosine rule:

(a) to find a side when you are given two sides and the angle between them.

or $\cos B=\dfrac{c^2+a^2-b^2}{2ca}$

or $\cos C=\dfrac{a^2+b^2-c^2}{2ab}$

(b) to find an angle when you know the lengths of the three sides. In this case the cosine rule is used in this form:

$$\cos A=\frac{b^2+c^2-a^2}{2bc}$$

> Remember to draw a realistic sketch.

Example

(a) In triangle ABC, $c=10$ cm, $a=12$ cm, angle $B=20°$. Calculate the length of side b.

$$b^2=c^2+a^2-2ca\cos B$$
$$b^2=12^2+10^2-2\times12\times10\times\cos 20$$
$$b^2=\sqrt{144+100-640\cos 20}$$
$$=4.3\text{ cm}$$

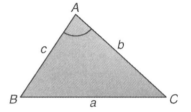

(b) Find the angles of a triangle with sides 4 cm, 5 cm and 6 cm.

$$\cos A=\frac{b^2+c^2-a^2}{2bc}$$
$$=\frac{4^2+5^2-6^2}{2\times4\times5}$$
$$=0.125$$
$$\therefore\quad A=\cos^{-1}0.125$$
$$=82.8°$$

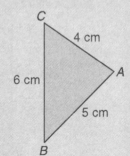

Using the sine rule to find angle B:

$$\frac{\sin B}{4} = \frac{\sin 82.8}{6}$$

$$\sin B = \frac{4 \times \sin 82.8}{6}$$

$$= 0.6614$$

$$\therefore \quad B = \sin^{-1} 0.6614$$

$$= 41.4°$$

$$\therefore \quad C = 180° - 41.4° - 82.8° = 55.8°$$

1 Find the missing angles and sides for each of these triangles:

(a)

(b)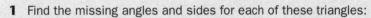

(c)

(d)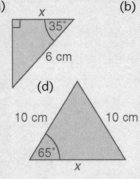

(e)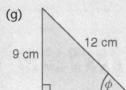

(f)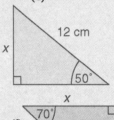

(g)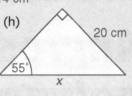

(h)

2 A square-based pyramid has base ABCD and vertex V vertically above the middle of the base. AB = 10 cm and VC = 20 cm.

Find:

(a) AC
(b) the height of the pyramid
(c) the angle between VC and the base ABCD.

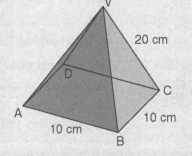

3 Find the areas of the following triangles:

(a)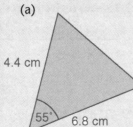

(b)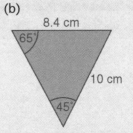

(c)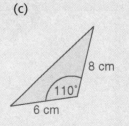

PROGRESS CHECK

PROGRESS CHECK

4 Find the sides and angles marked with letters in these triangles. Give angles to the nearest degree and lengths to 1 d.p.

(a)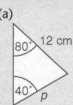

(b)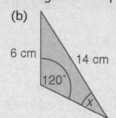

(c)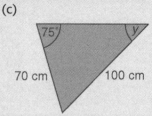

5 A yacht leaves port and sails 50 km due east. It then changes direction and sails another 50 km on a bearing of 200°.
How far from the port is the yacht now?

6 A triangle ABC has the following measurements:
Angle $B = 49°$; Angle $C = 62°$; side $BC = 6.2$ cm
(a) Calculate the length of side AC.
(b) Calculate the area of the triangle.

7 In triangle ABC, $AB = 4$ cm, $AC = 6$ cm and angle $A = 53°$. Calculate BC and angle B.

8 A triangle has sides of 6 cm, 7 cm and 8 cm.
Find the largest angle of the triangle.

1 (a) 4.9 cm (b) 38.2° (c) 9.2 cm (d) $\frac{x}{2} = 10 \cos 65$ so $x = 8.5$ cm
  (e) 37.5° (f) 11.3 cm (g) 48.6° (h) 24.4 cm
2 (a) AC = 14.14 cm (b) height = 18.7 cm (c) 69.3°
3 (a) 12.25 cm² (b) 39.47 cm² (c) 22.55 cm²
4 (a) 18.4 cm (b) 21.8° (c) 42.5°
5 57.4 km
6 (a) 5.0 cm (b) 13.7 cm²
7 BC = 4.8 cm angle B = 85.4° **8** 75.5°

3.5 Angles in lines and polygons

LEARNING SUMMARY

After studying this section, you will be able to:

● **understand angle properties of angle at a point and on lines**
● **deduce angle properties of triangles and quadrilaterals**
● **use angle properties of other polygons**
● **calculate unknown angles using the above properties**

Angles

KEY POINT Remember that there are 360° in a circle, so the lines around a point must add up to 360°.

Here, $x = 360° - 318° = 42°$.

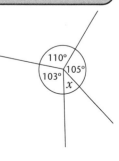

KEY POINT
The angles on each side of a straight line must add up to 180°.

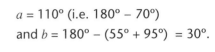

Here:

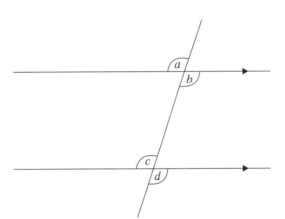

$a = 110°$ (i.e. $180° - 70°$)
and $b = 180° - (55° + 95°) = 30°$.

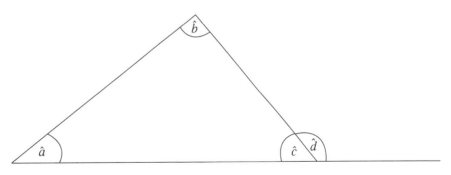

For parallel lines:

$\hat{a} = \hat{b}$ and these are known as **opposite angles**,

$\hat{a} = \hat{d}$ and these are known as **alternate angles**,

$\hat{a} = \hat{c}$ and these are known as **similar angles**.

For any triangle:

1. the sum of the internal angles must be 180°,
    so $\hat{a} + \hat{b} + \hat{c} = 180°$,
2. the sum of two internal angles equals the opposite external angle,
    so $\hat{d} = \hat{a} + \hat{b}$.

Polygons

The word 'polygon' means 'many sided', and the simplest polygon is a triangle, whose internal angles add up to 180°.

A polygon with 4 sides is a **quadrilateral**.

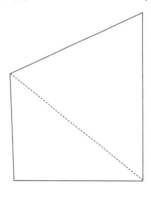

This quadrilateral can be divided into 2 triangles, so the sum of its internal angles = 2(180°) = 360°.

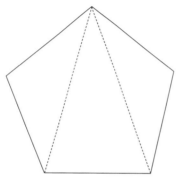

A 5-sided polygon, or **pentagon** can be divided into 3 triangles, so the sum of its internal angles = 540°.

> **KEY POINT**
>
> In general, a polygon with *n* sides can be divided into (*n* – 2) triangles, and so the sum of its internal angles is = (*n* – 2)180°.

A polygon which has all sides of equal length and all internal angles of equal measure is said to be a **regular polygon**.

Consider a regular **hexagon**.

(Sum of internal angles = 720°. All internal angles are equal, so each angle is equal to $\frac{720°}{6} = 120°$)

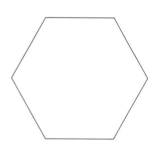

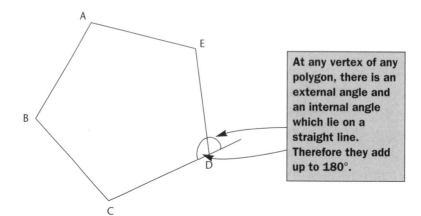

At any vertex of any polygon, there is an external angle and an internal angle which lie on a straight line. Therefore they add up to 180°.

All these external angles add up to 360°. To understand this, imagine that you were walking around this **octagon**.

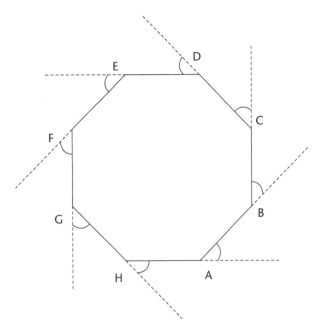

If you started from A, facing B, you would (on walling to B) have to turn through one external angle to walk to C. Then turn through another external angle to walk to D, and so on to get back to A. At A, you would have to turn through a last external angle to face B again.

In effect, you would have walked around a full circle.

Example

The sum of the internal angles of a regular polygon is 3960°. How many sides does it have?

However many sides it has, the sum of its external angles will always be 360°. So the sum of internal + external angles is 3960° + 360° = 4320°. Each internal–external angle pair adds up to 180°, so there are $\frac{4320}{180} = 24$ such pairs, and hence 24 sides.

---

1 What is the sum of the internal angles of a decagon (10 sides)?

2 Calculate the sum of the internal angles of a regular dodecahedron (12 sides).

3 The sum of the internal angles of a regular polygon is 6300°. How many sides does it have.

3 37 sides.
2 1800°
1 $(10 - 2)180° = 1440°$.

3.6 Circles

LEARNING SUMMARY

After studying this section, you will be able to:

- *find angles in a cyclic quadrilateral*
- *find angles at the centre and circumference of a circle*
- *find angles between a radius and a chord*
- *find the angle between a tangent and a chord*
- *find the angle in the alternate segment*

Cyclic quadrilaterals

A **cyclic quadrilateral** is a quadrilateral drawn inside a circle so that its corners lie on the circumference of the circle.

You should know that:

(a) the **opposite** angles of a cyclic quadrilateral sum to 180°

i.e. $a + c = 180°$
$b + d = 180°$

(b) the **exterior** angle of a cyclic quadrilateral is equal to the **interior opposite** angle

i.e. $e = c$

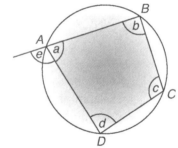

Angle theorems

(a) The angle at the circumference subtended by a diameter is 90°. This is usually stated as 'The angle in a semicircle = 90°'.

This can be proved as follows:

The lines OA, OP and OB are equal (radii of circle).

Triangles AOP and BOP are isosceles.

Therefore in triangle APB:

$a + a + b + b = 180°$

i.e. $2(a + b) = 180°$

therefore angle $APB = a + b = 90°$

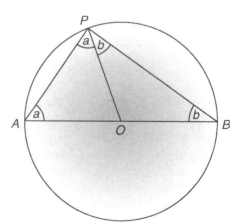

> **You need to remember these results.**

(b) The angle at the centre of a circle is twice the angle at the circumference.

Angle $AOB = 2 \times$ angle ACB

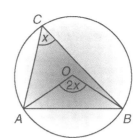

(c) Angles subtended by the same arc or chord are equal.

In Figure 1 the angles marked x are equal and subtended by chord CD, or arc CD.

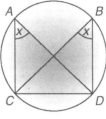

Fig 1

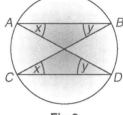

Fig 2

In Figure 2 the angles marked x are equal, being subtended by chord BD and the angles marked y are equal, being subtended by chord AC.

Examples

(a) In this diagram O is the centre of the circle. Calculate the value of angle a.

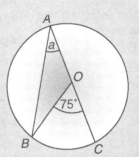

Angle $a = 37.5°$ (angle at the centre = $2 \times$ angle at the circumference)

(b) Calculate the angles marked with letters.

angle $a = 50°$ (angles subtended by the same arc)

angle $b = 100°$ (angle at centre = twice angle at circumference)

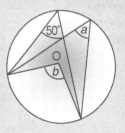

Chord theorems

The line joining the mid-point of a chord to the centre of a circle is perpendicular to the chord. This can be proved using congruent triangles.

AB is a chord to the circle centre O.

X is the mid-point of AB. In triangles OXA and OXB:

$OA = OB$ (radii)

$AX = XB$ (x is the mid-point)

OX is common.

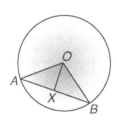

∴ Triangles OXA and OXB are congruent (SSS).

∴ angle $OXA =$ angle $OXB = 90°$

Tangents

There are two theorems for tangents that you need to know.

(a) Tangents drawn from the same point to the same circle are equal in length. They subtend equal angles at the centre of the circle and they make equal angles with the straight line joining the centre of the circle to the point.

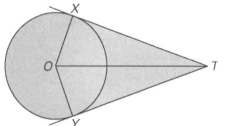

$TX = TY$

Angle XOT = angle YOT

Angle OTX = angle OTY

Angle OXT = angle OYT = 90°

(b) The angle between a tangent and a chord drawn from the point of contact is equal to any angle subtended by the chord in the alternate segment.

Angle BXT = angle BAX

This fact can be proved as follows:

Angle ABX = 90° (angle in a semicircle)

Angle OXT = 90° (angle between a diameter and a tangent)

Angle AXB = 90° − angle BXT

but angle AXB + angle BAX + angle ABX

= 180° (angle sum of triangle)

i.e. angle AXB + angle BAX = 90°

∴   90° − angle BXT + angle BAX = 90°

∴   angle BXT = angle BAX

> The point of contact is the point where the tangent touches the circle.

> You need to remember the results for chords and tangents.

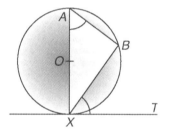

Examples

(a) Find angle a.

Angle OYT = 90°

Angle OYX = 40° (isosceles triangle)

∴   angle a = 50°

(b) Find angles a and b.

Angle a = 70°

Angle b = 50° (both are angles in alternate segment)

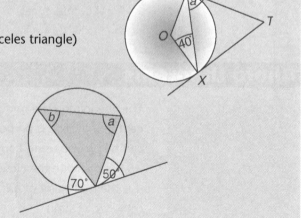

1 In each of the following diagrams O is the centre of the circle. Calculate the angles marked with letters.

(a)

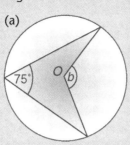

(b)

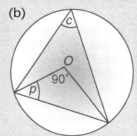

(c)

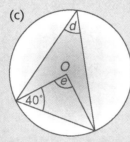

(d)

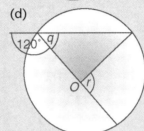

2 In each of the following diagrams O is the centre of the circle. Calculate the angles marked with letters.

(a)

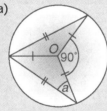

(b)

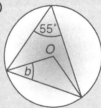

(c)

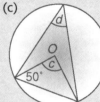

(d)

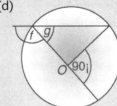

(e)

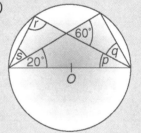

PROGRESS CHECK

In the following questions calculate the angles marked with letters. O is the centre of each circle.

X and Y are the points of contact of the tangents to each circle.

3 (a)

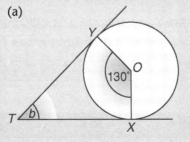

(b)

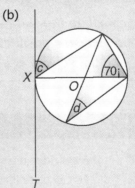

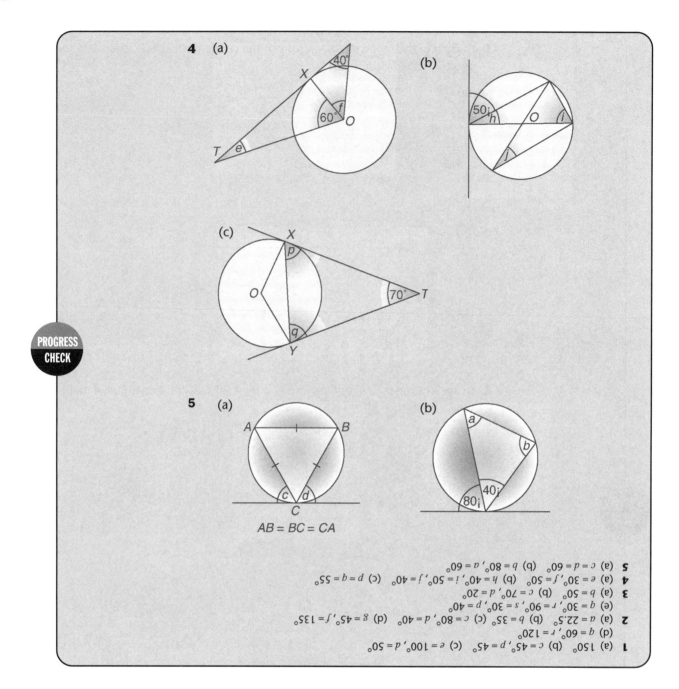

PROGRESS CHECK

1 (a) 150° (b) *c* = 45°, *p* = 45° (c) *e* = 100°, *d* = 50°
  (d) *g* = 60°, *r* = 120°
2 (a) *u* = 22.5° (b) *b* = 35° (c) *c* = 80°, *d* = 40° (d) *g* = 45°, *f* = 135°
  (e) *q* = 30°, *r* = 90°, *s* = 30°, *p* = 40°
3 (a) *b* = 50° (b) *c* = 70°, *d* = 20°
4 (a) *e* = 30°, *f* = 50° (b) *h* = 40°, *i* = 50°, *j* = 40° (c) *p* = *q* = 55°
5 (a) *c* = *d* = 60° (b) *b* = 80°, *a* = 60°

3.7 3-D shapes

LEARNING SUMMARY

After studying this section, you will be able to:

- **calculate the surface area and volume of a cylinder**
- **recognise a prism as a solid with a uniform cross-section**
- **find the volume of a prism, a pyramid, a cone and a sphere**

Cylinders

A **cylinder** is a shape, often encountered in practical life.
To calculate its volume, think of it as a stack of thin coins.

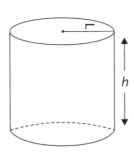

The surface area of each coin is πr^2 (the area of circle) and if each coin ha a thickness 't', the volume of metal in the coin is $\pi r^2 t$.

However, if each coin in the stack has the same thickness t, then the total of these thicknesses is h.

So the volume of the cylinder is $\pi r^2 h$.

Be careful: if the cylinder is open at both ends, its surface area is $2\pi rh$.

The curved surface area = circumference of a coin × height = $2\pi rh$.

If it has a base, i.e. it is closed at one end, we must add one πr^2, which is the area of a circular bottom. If the cylinder is closed at both ends or is solid, we add $2\pi r^2$:

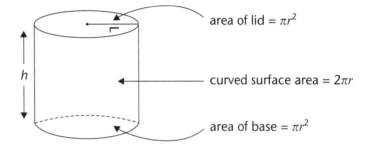

area of lid = πr^2

curved surface area = $2\pi r$

area of base = πr^2

Example

A thin aluminium can of soup is 20 cm tall and has a radius of 3.5 cm.

(a) How much aluminium was used to make the can?

(b) How much soup would the can hold, when filled to the brim?

(a) Area of a closed can $= 2\pi r^2 + 2\pi rh = 2\left(\dfrac{22}{7}\right)(3.5)^2 + 2\left(\dfrac{22}{7}\right)(3.5)(20)$

$= \dfrac{44 \times 3.5 \times 3.5}{7} + \dfrac{44 \times 3.5 \times 20}{7} = 77 + 440 = 517 \text{ cm}^2.$

(b) Volume of soup $= \pi r^2 h = \dfrac{22}{7} \times 3.5 \times 3.5 \times 20 = 770 \text{ cm}^3.$

You should also know and be able to use the formulae for the areas of the following shapes: parallelogram, rhombus, trapezium. These may be needed when calculating the volumes of prisms.

Prisms and other shapes

If a solid also has a uniform cross-section; that is, the cross-sectional area is the same throughout its length then the solid is a prism.

You should also know the formulae for the volumes of the cone and the pyramid (although you would be given them in an examination).

Pyramid

volume $= \dfrac{1}{3} \times$ base area $\times$ perpendicular height

Note the similarity.

Cone

volume = $\frac{1}{3}$ × base area × perpendicular height

$= \frac{1}{3}\pi r^2 h$

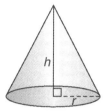

Example

A block of metal is shaped as shown below. Calculate the surface area and volume of the block.

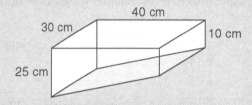

Area of trapezium at the front	$= \frac{1}{2} \times (25 + 10) \times 40$
	$= 700 \text{ cm}^2$
Area of trapezium at the back	$= 700 \text{ cm}^2$
Total area of rectangles at the side	$= 25 \times 30 + 10 \times 30$
	$= 1050 \text{ cm}^2$
Area of rectangle at the top	$= 30 \times 40$
	$= 1200 \text{ cm}^2$
Area of rectangle at base	$= 30 \times \sqrt{15^2 + 40^2}$
	$= 30 \times 42.72$
	$= 1282 \text{ cm}^2$ (to nearest whole number)
Therefore total surface area	$= 4932 \text{ cm}^2$
Volume	= cross-sectional area × length
	$= 700 \times 30$
	$= 21\,000 \text{ cm}^3$

Example

A bucket is in the shape of a frustum of a hollow cone and is made by removing a 10 cm part of the cone as shown.
Find the volume of the bucket.

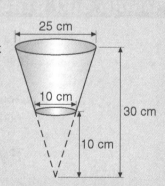

Volume of complete cone

$= \frac{1}{3}$ × base area × perpendicular height

$= \frac{1}{3} \times \pi \times 12.5^2 \times 30$

$= 4908.7 \text{ cm}^3$

Volume of cone removed

$= \frac{1}{3} \times \pi \times 5^2 \times 10$

$= 261.8 \text{ cm}^3$

Volume remaining = 4647 cm³
(to the nearest whole number)

1 Find the surface area and volume of a cuboid measuring 210 mm by 100 mm by 70 mm.

2 A pyramid has a square base of side 12 cm and a height of 15 cm. Find its volume.

3 A cone has a base radius of 3.8 cm and is 8 cm high. Find its volume.

4 Find the volume of a sphere of radius 15 cm. (Volume of a sphere = $\frac{4}{3}\pi r^3$.)

1 854 cm², 1470 cm³ 2 720 cm³ 3 121 cm³ 4 14 100 cm³ (3 s.f.)

3.8 Transformations

After studying this section, you will be able to:
● **specify reflections, translations, rotations and enlargements**

Reflections and translations

The simplest transformations are (a) **reflections** in horizontal lines (such as $y = 0$ (the x-axis) or $y = 3$); or in vertical lines (such as $x = 0$ (the y-axis), or $x = -2$), and (b) **translations**.

Reflections

Note that reflection and translation preserve the size and shape of the object.

This diagram shows a flag, ABCDE, reflected in the lines (a) $x = 1$, (b) $y = 0$, and (c) $y = -x$

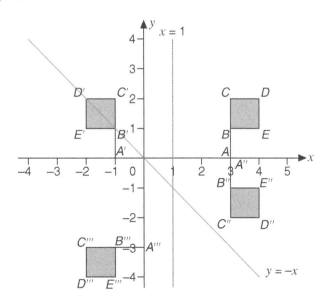

Vector notation and translations

> **KEY POINT** A **vector** is a quantity which has both magnitude (size), and direction.

Vectors are used to represent displacement, velocity, force, momentum, acceleration.

In geometry vectors are used to represent displacement.

In a diagram a vector can be shown in two ways:

(a) by using capital letters at each end and an arrow showing the direction.

This is the vector $\overrightarrow{AB}$.

The magnitude of the vector is written as $|\overrightarrow{AB}|$.

(b) by using a small letter and an arrow showing direction.

This is the vector **a**.

In hand-writing it is shown as $\underline{a}$ or $\underset{\sim}{a}$.

Vectors can be used to represent a move from one point to another, i.e. to describe a translation.

The move represented by the vector a can be written as a column vector:

$$\mathbf{a} = \begin{pmatrix} x \\ y \end{pmatrix}$$

Example

The column vectors which give the translation of point A to points B, C, D, E are:

to B $\begin{pmatrix} 2 \\ 0 \end{pmatrix}$, to C $\dfrac{1}{2}^{x}$, to D $\begin{pmatrix} -1 \\ -1 \end{pmatrix}$, to E $\begin{pmatrix} -2 \\ 3 \end{pmatrix}$.

Combinations of translations can also be described using vectors.

Example

Translating the triangle ABC using the vector $\begin{pmatrix} 5 \\ 2 \end{pmatrix}$ gives the triangle $A'B'C'$. Translating triangle $A'B'C'$ using the vector $\begin{pmatrix} -2 \\ 3 \end{pmatrix}$ gives the triangle $A''B''C''$.

The translation $\begin{pmatrix} 3 \\ 5 \end{pmatrix}$ shows the movement of triangle ABC to triangle $A''B''C''$, and combining the two vectors gives $\begin{pmatrix} 5 \\ 2 \end{pmatrix} + \begin{pmatrix} -2 \\ 3 \end{pmatrix} = \begin{pmatrix} 3 \\ 5 \end{pmatrix}$.

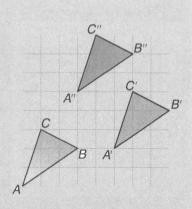

Rotations

KEY POINT By convention an anti-clockwise rotation is positive and a clockwise rotation is negative.

To describe a rotation requires three pieces of information:

(a) the angle of the rotation;   (b) the direction of the rotation;   (c) the centre of the rotation.

> Rotation preserves shape and size so the rotated shapes are congruent to the original shape.

Example

(a) rotating triangle ABC through $-90°$, i.e. clockwise, about $(0, 0)$ gives the image $A'B'C'$.

(b) rotating triangle $A'B'C'$ through $180°$ about $(0, 0)$ gives $A''B''C''$.

(c) It is possible to define a single transformation to rotate ABC to $A''B''C''$: a rotation of $90°$ about $(0, 0)$.

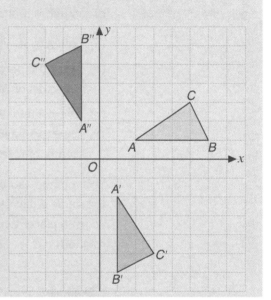

It is a straightforward process to rotate a shape through any size of angle:

Example

Rotate triangle ABC through $40°$ about the point O. Label the image $A'B'C'$.

Draw lines OA, OB, OC. Measure the distances OA, OB, OC; draw lines OA', OB', OC' so that $OA = OA'$, $OB = OB'$, $OC = OC'$, and the angles $AOA' = BOB' = COC' = 40°$. Alternatively measure OA and draw $OA' = OA$ and $AOA' = 40°$ and use tracing paper to complete the image.

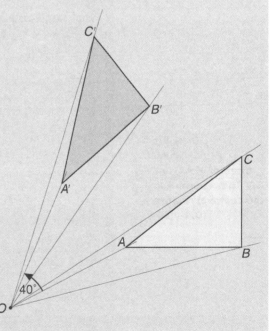

To find the centre of rotation you need to know the position of a point on the object, say A, and its image, A'. The centre of rotation must be the same distance from A and A'

Join A to A' and construct the perpendicular bisector of the line AA'. The centre of rotation, O, will lie on this line, but, to fix the centre requires the process to be repeated for another point and its image, i.e. B and B'.

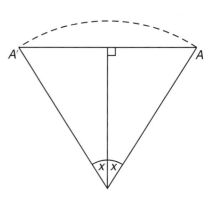

Thus for an object, such as triangle ABC, and its image, triangle $A'B'C'$, the centre of rotation is found as follows:

(a) join A to A' and B to B'

(b) draw the perpendicular bisectors of lines AA' and BB'

(c) the point where these bisectors intersect is the centre of rotation, O.

This method can be used to find the single equivalent rotation which replaces two or more rotations.

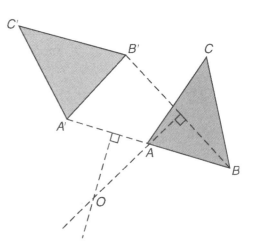

Example

Rotate triangle ABC through 30° about the origin. Label its image $A'B'C'$.
Rotate triangle $A'B'C'$ through 70° about the point P, (0, 2). Label this image $A''B''C''$.
What single rotation will map triangle ABC onto triangle $A''B''C''$?

Draw the perpendicular bisector of AA″ and CC″ They intersect at the centre of rotation (0.4, 1.6).

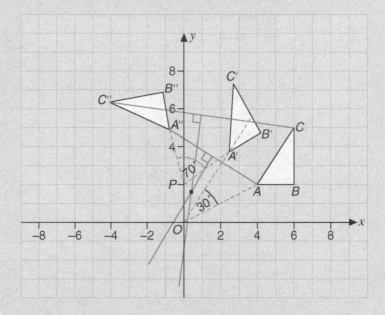

The single rotation is 103° about the point (0.4, 1.6).

Enlargements

To carry out an enlargement requires two pieces of information:

(a) the scale factor (b) the centre of the enlargement.

Example

Rectangle *ABCD* is enlarged by a scale factor of 2; the centre of enlargement is the origin.

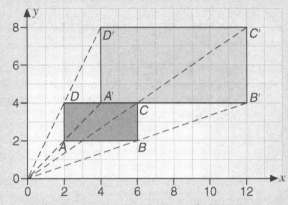

This means that $OA' = 2 \times OA$ measured along *OA* extended

$$OB' = 2 \times OB \text{ measured along } OB \text{ extended}$$
$$OC' = 2 \times OC \text{ measured along } OC \text{ extended}$$
$$OD' = 2 \times OD \text{ measured along } OD \text{ extended}$$

The image *A'B'C'D'* is four times the size of the object *ABCD*.

If the scale factor is negative the image is on the opposite side of the centre of enlargement, and the image is inverted, as shown in the next example.

Example

Triangle *A*(2, 2), *B*(4, 2), *C*(2, 5) is enlarged by a scale factor −2. The centre of enlargement is the point *P*, (0, 1). This is shown in the diagram where, for example $PA' = 2 \times PA$ as measured along the line *AP* extended, that is to the left of *P*.

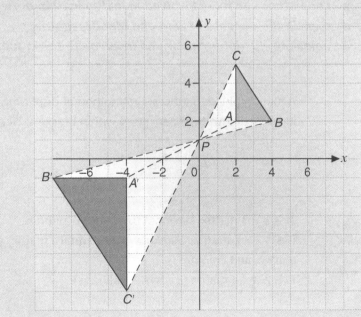

PROGRESS
CHECK

1 Draw a triangle ABC at $A(1, 2)$, $B(3, 5)$, $C(6, 2)$.
  (a) Find the image of triangle ABC under a 90° rotation, anticlockwise about the origin.
  (b) Find the image of triangle ABC under a 90° rotation, clockwise about the point $(2, -2)$.

2 Draw a triangle with vertices $A(1, 2)$, $B(1, 6)$ $C(1, 2)$. Rotate this triangle through 70° about the point $(1, 2)$.

3 Draw a triangle $A(4, 4)$, $B(1, 4)$, $C(1, 2)$ and rotate it through 40° about the origin giving triangle $A'B'C'$. Rotate triangle $A'B'C'$ through $-70°$ about the point $(-1, -1)$.
  What single rotation is equivalent to the combination of these two rotations?

4 Draw a set of axes, the x-axis from -16 to $+6$, the y-axis from -6 to $+4$. Draw a quadrilateral with coordinates $A(2, 2)$, $B(5, 0)$, $C(5, -1)$, $D(2, -1)$. Draw the enlargement of $ABCD$ by a scale factor of -3 with centre of enlargement, the origin.

1 (a) $A'(-2, 1)$, $B'(-5, 3)$, $C'(-2, 6)$
  (b) $A'(6, -1)$, $B'(9, -3)$, $C'(6, -6)$
2 $A'(1, 2)$, $B'(-2.8, 3.3)$, $C'(-1.1, 4.8)$
3 30° about the point $(-1, 1, 3)$
4 $A'(-6, -6)$, $B'(-15, 0)$, $C'(-15, 3)$, $D'(-6, 3)$

3.9 Matrices

LEARNING
SUMMARY

After studying this section, you will be able to:

- *perform arithmetic operations involving matrices*
- *understand the rules involved in multiplication of two matrices*
- *explain the concept of zero and identity matrices*
- *calculate the determinant and inverse of* (2 × 2) *matrices*

A matrix (plural: matrices) is a method of displaying and manipulating numbers in **row-column form**, enclosed within brackets. Here are some matrices.

$$\underline{A} = \begin{pmatrix} 3 & 4 & -1 \\ 0 & 2 & 5 \end{pmatrix} \quad \underline{B} = \begin{pmatrix} 1 & 4 \\ 6 & -3 \end{pmatrix} \quad \underline{C} = \begin{pmatrix} 5 & 4 & 0 & -5 \\ 8 & -2 & 4 & 0 \\ 7 & -1 & 3 & 8 \end{pmatrix}.$$

Matrices are usually named with capital letters in bold print, or underlined.

$\underline{A}$ is 2 × 3 matrix, having 2 rows and 3 columns.
$\underline{B}$ is a 2 × 2 matrix, also known as a **square** matrix, since it has the same number of rows and columns.
$\underline{C}$ is a 3 × 4 matrix (3 rows, 4 columns).

Operations on matrices

We add matrices by adding together the corresponding terms:

$$\begin{pmatrix} 2 & 3 & 5 \\ 1 & 4 & -4 \end{pmatrix} + \begin{pmatrix} -4 & 0 & 2 \\ -2 & -5 & 1 \end{pmatrix} = \begin{pmatrix} -2 & 3 & 7 \\ -1 & -1 & -3 \end{pmatrix}$$

Similar process is followed for subtraction:

$$\begin{pmatrix} -3 & 1 \\ 2 & 5 \\ 4 & 1 \end{pmatrix} - \begin{pmatrix} 2 & -4 \\ 1 & 2 \\ 3 & 0 \end{pmatrix} = \begin{pmatrix} -5 & 5 \\ 1 & 3 \\ 1 & 1 \end{pmatrix}$$

four minus   three equals   one

> **KEY POINT** For addition and subtraction, the type of matrices must be identical, i.e. they must have the same numbers of rows and columns.

When multiplying matrices, we do the following:

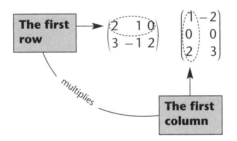

The first row 'dives in' and multiplies the first column as follows:
$2(1) + 1(0) + 2(2) = 2.$

Then the first row is multiplied with the second column:
$2(-2) + 1(0) + 0(3) = -4.$
The second row is multiplied with the first column:
$3(1) + -1(0) + 2(2) = 7$
and the second row is multiplied with the second column:
$3(-2) + -1(0) + 2(3) = 0.$

Our final result is as follows:

$$\begin{pmatrix} 2 & 1 & 0 \\ 3 & -1 & 2 \end{pmatrix} \begin{pmatrix} 1 & -2 \\ 0 & 0 \\ 2 & 3 \end{pmatrix} = \begin{pmatrix} 2 & -4 \\ 7 & 0 \end{pmatrix}$$

This is a 2 × 3 matrix, and a 3 × 2 matrix   This is a 2 × 2 matrix

> **KEY POINT** To multiply matrices, the number of columns in the first matrix must equal the number of rows in the seconds.

Some more examples on matrix multiplication are as follows:

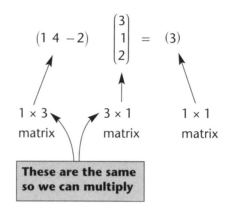

When we wish to multiply a matrix by a single number, we just multiply the matrix entries separately:

$$4\begin{pmatrix} 3 & 2 \\ -1 & 1 \end{pmatrix} = \begin{pmatrix} 12 & 8 \\ -4 & 4 \end{pmatrix}$$

Look what happens when we multiply a 2 × 2 (two row, two column) matrix by the matrix $\begin{pmatrix} 1 & 0 \\ 0 & 1 \end{pmatrix}$:

$$\begin{pmatrix} 3 & 4 \\ 1 & 2 \end{pmatrix}\begin{pmatrix} 1 & 0 \\ 0 & 1 \end{pmatrix} = \begin{pmatrix} 3 & 4 \\ 1 & 2 \end{pmatrix}$$

This matrix remains unchanged.

As $\begin{pmatrix} 1 & 0 \\ 0 & 1 \end{pmatrix}$ leaves the other matrix unchanged on multiplication, it is called the

identity matrix for multiplication.

For example:

$$\begin{pmatrix} 5 & 2 \\ 3 & -1 \end{pmatrix}\begin{pmatrix} 1 & 0 \\ 0 & 1 \end{pmatrix} = \begin{pmatrix} 5 & 2 \\ 3 & -1 \end{pmatrix}.$$

Determinant

We can find the **determinant** of a matrix as:

This is called the 'leading diagonal.'

(a) Multiply the numbers on the leading diagonal: $2 \times 5 = 10$.

(b) Multiply the numbers on the other diagonal : $4 \times 3 = 12$.

(c) Subtract (b) from (a): $10 - 12 = -2$.

(d) Interchange the leading diagonal numbers and change the signs on the numbers in the other diagonal. Before this new matrix, we place the multiplier 1/2, since the result of instruction 3 tells us that our matrix is 2 times bigger than the desired matrix.

From $\begin{pmatrix} 2 & 4 \\ 3 & 5 \end{pmatrix}$, we produce the matrix $\dfrac{-1}{2}\begin{pmatrix} -5 & 4 \\ 3 & -2 \end{pmatrix}$ and taking the minus

sign into the matrix, we get $\dfrac{1}{2}\begin{pmatrix} -5 & 4 \\ 3 & -2 \end{pmatrix}$.

Now:

$$\frac{1}{2}\begin{pmatrix} -5 & 4 \\ 3 & -2 \end{pmatrix}\begin{pmatrix} 2 & 4 \\ 3 & 5 \end{pmatrix} = \frac{1}{2}\begin{pmatrix} 2 & 0 \\ 0 & 2 \end{pmatrix} = \begin{pmatrix} 1 & 0 \\ 0 & 1 \end{pmatrix}$$

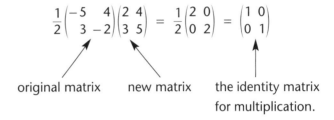

original matrix   new matrix   the identity matrix for multiplication.

The new matrix is the **multiplication inverse** of the first, as we get the **identity matrix** $\begin{pmatrix} 1 & 0 \\ 0 & 1 \end{pmatrix}$ on multiplying them together.

Example

Let $P = \begin{pmatrix} 3 & 2 \\ 5 & 7 \end{pmatrix}$.

Then to get P^{-1} we carry out the operation:

$$3(7) = 2(5) = 11, \quad \text{so } P^{-1} = \frac{1}{11}\begin{pmatrix} 7 & -2 \\ -5 & 3 \end{pmatrix}.$$

Thus, $P^{-1}x \; P = \dfrac{1}{11}\begin{pmatrix} 7 & -2 \\ -5 & 3 \end{pmatrix}\begin{pmatrix} 3 & 2 \\ 5 & 7 \end{pmatrix} = \dfrac{1}{11}\begin{pmatrix} 11 & 0 \\ 0 & 11 \end{pmatrix} = \begin{pmatrix} 1 & 0 \\ 0 & 1 \end{pmatrix}.$

Check for yourself that if:

$$A = \begin{pmatrix} 4 & 7 \\ 2 & -9 \end{pmatrix}, \quad \text{then } A^{-1} = \frac{-1}{50}\begin{pmatrix} -9 & -7 \\ -2 & 4 \end{pmatrix}$$

and if $B = \begin{pmatrix} -2 & 3 \\ 4 & -6 \end{pmatrix}$, then $B^{-1} = \dfrac{1}{4}\begin{pmatrix} -8 & -3 \\ -4 & -2 \end{pmatrix}.$

Note that we cannot find the inverse of the matrix $\begin{pmatrix} 2 & 4 \\ 4 & 8 \end{pmatrix}$ because $2(8) - (4)(4) = 0$.

Such matrices are said to be **singular**.

PROGRESS CHECK

1 Multiply:

$$\begin{pmatrix} 2 & 5 & 7 \\ 4 & 3 & 6 \end{pmatrix} \begin{pmatrix} 3 & 2 \\ -4 & -5 \\ 1 & -2 \end{pmatrix}.$$

2 Find the inverse of $\begin{pmatrix} 3 & -7 \\ -2 & 6 \end{pmatrix}.$

2 $\dfrac{1}{4}\begin{pmatrix} 6 & 7 \\ 2 & 3 \end{pmatrix}$

1 $\begin{pmatrix} 6 & -19 \\ -7 & -35 \end{pmatrix}$

3.10 Area and volume

LEARNING SUMMARY

After studying this section, you will be able to:
- *distinguish between formulae for length, area and volume*
- *find areas and volumes of similar figures*

Dimensions

You need to be able to distinguish between the formulae for length, area and volume.

A formula involving one dimension, such as height, is a measurement of length, e.g. cm.

A formula involving two dimensions, such as width × length, is a measurement of area, e.g. cm^2.

A formula involving three dimensions, such as length × width × height, is a measurement of volume, e.g. cm^3.

Example

What quantities do the following represent?

(a) $\frac{4}{3}\pi r^3$ (b) $2\pi rh$

(a) $\frac{4}{3}\pi r^3$ includes $r \times r \times r$ i.e. three lengths multiplied together.

Therefore it represents a volume.

(b) $2\pi rh$ includes $r \times h$ i.e. a length × length, therefore it represents an area.

Areas and volumes of similar figures

If two figures are similar then the corresponding edges on those figures are in the same ratio.

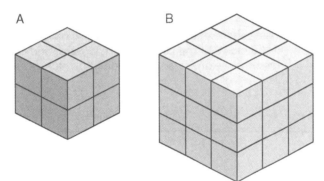

The ratio of the lengths of the sides of these two cubes is 2 : 3.

The area of a face of cube A is 4 square units.
The area of a face on cube B is 9 square units
The areas of the faces are in the ratio 4 : 9 i.e. $2^2 : 3^2$.
The total surface area of cube A is 6×4 square units = 24 square units, that for cube B is 6×9 square units i.e. 54 square units.
The ratio of the surface areas is 24 : 54 = 4 : 9 = $2^2 : 3^2$.
Thus it can be seen that the ratio of the areas of these similar figures is the ratio of the squares of the lengths of the sides.
In general terms:

if the ratio of the lengths is $a : b$ then the ratio of the areas is $a^2 : b^2$.

The volume of cube A = $2 \times 2 \times 2$ = 8 cubic units
The volume of cube B = $3 \times 3 \times 3$ = 27 cubic units
The ratio of the volumes = 8 : 27 = $2^3 : 3^3$.
In the same way, if the ratio of the lengths is $a : b$, then the ratio of the volumes is $a^3 : b^3$.

Example

Two similar cones are made, the larger cone has a diameter twice that of the smaller cone. The smaller cone has a surface area of 500 cm^2 and a volume of 130 cm^3. Calculate the surface area and volume of the larger cone.

Ratio of lengths = 2 : 1
∴ Ratio of areas = $2^2 : 1^2 = 4 : 1$
Thus surface area of larger cone = 4 × 500 = 2000 cm^2.
Ratio of volumes = $2^3 : 1^3 = 8 : 1$
Thus volume of larger cone = 8 × 130 cm^3 = 1040 cm^3.

PROGRESS CHECK

1 Which of the following represent areas and which volumes?

(a) $\frac{1}{2}bh$ (b) $\frac{1}{2}ab\sin C$ (c) $2\pi r^2(r+h)$ (d) $\frac{4}{3}\pi(r^2+h^2)$ (e) $2\pi r^2 + 2\pi rh$

2 Two similar cylinders have heights of 3 cm and 6 cm respectively. If the volume of the smaller cylinder is 30 cm^3, find the volume of the larger cylinder.

3 Two spheres made of the same metal have weights of 32 kg and 108 kg. If the radius of the larger sphere is 9 cm, find the radius of the small sphere (assume weights are proportional to volumes).

2 240 cm^3 **3** 6 cm
1 (a) area (b) area (c) volume (d) area (e) area

3.11 Vectors

After studying this section, you will be able to:

LEARNING SUMMARY

- **identify the zero vector and unit vectors**
- **understand equal and inverse vectors**
- **know what a scalar is**
- **add and subtract vectors**
- **solve problems using vectors**
- **describe translations using vectors**
- **calculate magnitudes of vectors**

Zero vector and unit vectors

> Vectors were introduced earlier when looking at translations.

A vector with magnitude 0 is called the **zero vector**, written **0**. A vector with magnitude 1 is called a **unit vector**.

Vectors are equal if they have the same magnitude and the same direction.
a = b

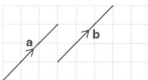

Inverse vectors

The **inverse** of a vector is a vector of equal magnitude but in the opposite direction. The inverse of $-\overrightarrow{AB}$ is $-\overrightarrow{AB}$ or $\overrightarrow{BA}$ and the inverse of **a** is **−a**.

Scalars

Scalars are quantities which have magnitude but not direction. You can multiply a vector by a scalar to produce another vector.

For example, multiplying vector **a** by **2** gives a vector twice the length of **a** and parallel to **a**.

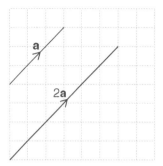

If $\mathbf{a} = \begin{pmatrix} 3 \\ 3 \end{pmatrix}$ then $2\mathbf{a} = 2\begin{pmatrix} 3 \\ 3 \end{pmatrix} = \begin{pmatrix} 6 \\ 6 \end{pmatrix}$

Vector addition and subtraction

When two vectors are added or subtracted to produce a third vector this vector is called the **resultant**. The resultant vector is marked with a double arrowhead.

Triangle law

To add two vectors, apply the first vector then apply the second vector.
$\overrightarrow{AB} + \overrightarrow{BC} = \overrightarrow{AC}$
or $\mathbf{a} + \mathbf{b} = \mathbf{c}$
This is known as the **triangle law**.

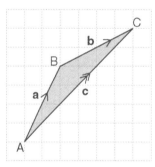

Parallelogram law

The **parallelogram law** shows that going from A to C via B is the same as going from A to C via D.
In other words:
$\overrightarrow{AB} + \overrightarrow{BC} = \overrightarrow{AC}$ is the same as

$\overrightarrow{AD} + \overrightarrow{DC} = \overrightarrow{AC}$
or $\mathbf{a} + \mathbf{b} = \mathbf{b} + \mathbf{a} = \mathbf{c}$

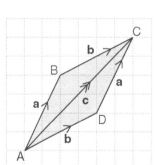

Subtracting a vector is the same as adding its inverse:
a − b is the same as **a + (−b)**.

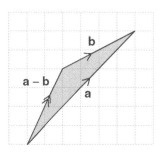

Vectors can be used to prove geometric properties and relationships

Example

In the triangle ABC the points X and Y are the mid-points of AB and AC. Show that line XY is parallel to BC and half its length.

Let $\quad \overrightarrow{AX} = \mathbf{a}$ and $\overrightarrow{AY} = \mathbf{b}$

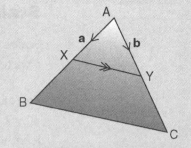

$$\therefore \quad \overrightarrow{XY} = \overrightarrow{XA} + \overrightarrow{AY}$$
$$= -\mathbf{a} + \mathbf{b} = \mathbf{b} - \mathbf{a}$$
$$\overrightarrow{AX} = \tfrac{1}{2}\overrightarrow{AB}$$

so $\quad \overrightarrow{AB} = 2\overrightarrow{AX}$
$$= 2\mathbf{a}$$
$$\overrightarrow{AY} = \tfrac{1}{2}\overrightarrow{AC}$$

so $\quad \overrightarrow{AC} = 2\overrightarrow{AY} = 2\mathbf{b}$
$$\overrightarrow{BC} = \overrightarrow{BA} + \overrightarrow{AC}$$
$$= -2\mathbf{a} + 2\mathbf{b}$$
$$= -2(\mathbf{b} - \mathbf{a})$$

$$\therefore \quad \overrightarrow{BC} = 2\overrightarrow{XY} \text{ or } \overrightarrow{XY} = \tfrac{1}{2}\overrightarrow{BC}$$

$\therefore$ XY is parallel to BC and half its length.

Finding the resultant of two vectors is used to solve problems involving vector quantities such as force and velocity. Note that as force is a vector quantity then both magnitude and direction should be given.

Examples

(a) Find the resultant of two forces of magnitude 5 N and 12 N acting on a mass as shown in the diagram.

Add the two forces as vectors, joining them 'nose to tail'.

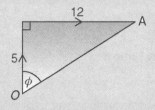

The magnitude of the resultant is found using Pythagoras and is 13 N. Find the angle using trigonometry.

$$\tan \phi = \frac{12}{5}$$

$$\therefore \quad \phi = 67.4°$$

The resultant is a force of 13 N at 67.4° to the direction of the 5 N force.

(b) An aircraft can fly at 300 mph in still air. The wind is blowing at 40 mph towards the south-east. If the aircraft heads due north what is the actual velocity relative to the ground?

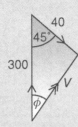

Actual velocity = velocity of aircraft + velocity of the air

Using cosine rule:

$V^2 = 300^2 + 40^2 - 2 \times 300 \times 40 \times \cos 45°$

$V = 273$ mph

Using sine rule $\dfrac{\sin \phi}{40} = \dfrac{\sin 45}{273}$

$\therefore$ $\phi = 6°$

Velocity is 273 mph at 006°.

PROGRESS CHECK

1 OABC is a quadrilateral, $\overrightarrow{OA} = \mathbf{a}, \overrightarrow{OB} = \mathbf{b}$ and $\overrightarrow{OC} = \mathbf{c}$.

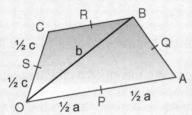

P, Q, R, S are the mid-points of OA, AB, BC and OC respectively.

(a) Find, in terms of **a**, **b** and **c**:
(i) $\overrightarrow{OP}$ (ii) $\overrightarrow{AB}$ (iii) $\overrightarrow{AQ}$ (iv) $\overrightarrow{PQ}$ (v) $\overrightarrow{SR}$

(b) Prove that PQ is parallel to SR.

(c) What type of quadrilateral is PQRS?

2 Two forces, P and Q, act on a mass. The resultant of P and Q is a force of magnitude 10 N and acts on a bearing of 055°. If force P has a magnitude of 12 N and acts due north find the magnitude and bearing of force Q.

2 10.3 N, 127.4°

(c) a parallelogram

1 (a) (i) $\frac{1}{2}$ **a** (ii) (**b** − **a**), (iii) $\frac{1}{2}$(**b** − **a**) (iv) $\frac{1}{2}$ **b** (v) $\frac{1}{2}$ **b**

Magnitude of vectors

We will now see how a **translation** can be expressed as a vector.

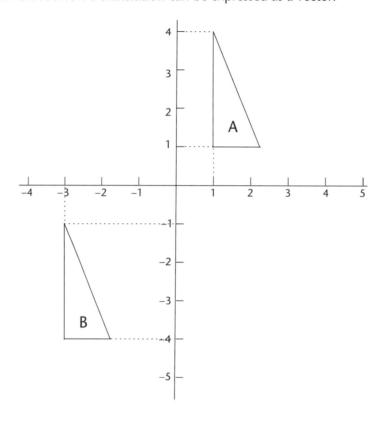

In the diagram, triangle A is mapped onto triangle B by the translation $\begin{pmatrix} -4 \\ -5 \end{pmatrix}$.

Triangle B is mapped onto triangle A by the translation $\begin{pmatrix} 4 \\ 5 \end{pmatrix}$.

Vectors have a magnitude (or size). Besides this, they also have a direction. If you look at the diagram above, you will see that mapping triangle B onto triangle A involves a slide of 4 units to the right (in the positive x-direction) and 5 units upwards (in the positive y-direction):

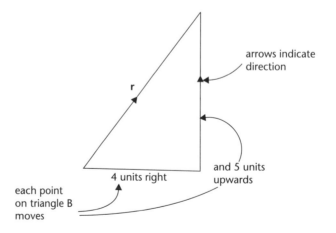

These two combined sideways and upward motions have the same effect as vector **r** in the above diagram. Vector **r** is called the **resultant** of the two vectors. Notice that its 'tail' is at the beginning of first vector and its head coincides with the arrowhead of the second vector.

Using Pythagoras theorem, the length of **r** must be $\sqrt{R^2 + 5^2} = \sqrt{16 + 25} = \sqrt{41}$ units.

We can represent a vector by $\begin{pmatrix} x \\ y \end{pmatrix}$, $\overrightarrow{XY}$ or XY.

1 Find the magnitude of the vectors:

(a) $\begin{pmatrix} -3 \\ 4 \end{pmatrix}$ (b) $\begin{pmatrix} -3 \\ -4 \end{pmatrix}$ (c) $\begin{pmatrix} 5 \\ 12 \end{pmatrix}$

(c) 13 units $(= \sqrt{5^2 + 12^2})$

(a) and (b) both have magnitude, or size, of 5 units, but in different directions.

Vectors can be used to map direction in space.

Look at this diagram:

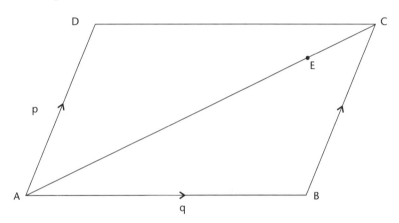

ABCD is a parallelogram, E is a point on AC such that AE: EC = 5:1. Also, $\overrightarrow{AD}$ = **p** and $\overrightarrow{AB}$ = **q**.

Now we are required to find magnitudes of

(a) $\overrightarrow{DC}$ (b) $\overrightarrow{AC}$ (c) $\overrightarrow{EC}$ (d) $\overrightarrow{EA}$ in terms of **p** and **q**.

We know that the line segment $\overrightarrow{AD}$ is called vector **p** and the line segment $\overrightarrow{AB}$ is the vector **q**.

This means that $\overrightarrow{DA}$ which is in the opposite direction to $\overrightarrow{AD}$ is −**p** and $\overrightarrow{AD}$ is −**q**.

Thus, we can get the answers as follows:

> **Remember that vectors are not localised in space.**

(a) Notice that $\overrightarrow{DC}$ is equal in length and in the same direction as $\overrightarrow{AB}$, so $\overrightarrow{DC}$ also equals **q**.

> **It is customary to write the vectors in alphabetical order.**

(b) $\overrightarrow{AC}$ can be represented as: $\overrightarrow{AB} + \overrightarrow{BC}$, or **q** + **p**.

Hence: $\overrightarrow{AC}$ = **p** + **q**.

(c) $\overrightarrow{EC}$ can be found by realising that, since AE : EC = 5 : 1, the length of EC is 1/6 of AC and in the direction of AC. So $\overrightarrow{EC} = \frac{1}{6}$ (**p** + **q**).

(d) $\vec{EA}$ is $\frac{5}{6}$ of $\vec{CA}$ or $\frac{5}{6}$ of $-(\vec{AC})$.

Hence $\vec{EA} = \frac{5}{6}$ [$-(\mathbf{p} + \mathbf{q})$], or $-\frac{5}{6}$ $(\mathbf{p} + \mathbf{q})$

Example

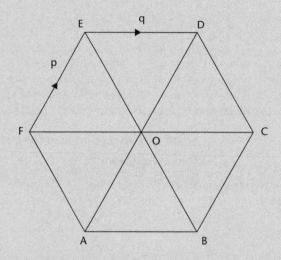

> A vector can be represented either by underlining or using an arrow overhead, a or $\vec{a}$

ABCDE is a regular hexagon with O as centre.

$\vec{FE} = \mathbf{p}$ and $\vec{ED} = \mathbf{q}$

Find (a) $\vec{CB}$ (b) $\vec{FC}$ (c) $\vec{DC}$ (d) $\vec{CA}$.

(a) $\vec{CB}$ is the same length as $\vec{FE}$, but in the opposite direction (FE and BC are parallel).

Hence $\vec{CB} = -\mathbf{p}$.

(b) $\vec{FC} = \vec{FO} + \vec{OC}$. Also, both FO and OC are of the same length and in the same direction as $\vec{ED}$.

$\therefore \vec{FC} = 2\mathbf{q}$

(c) $\vec{DC} = \vec{EO}$ in length and direction and $\vec{EO} = \vec{ED} + \vec{DO}$.

So $\vec{DC} = \vec{ED} + \vec{DO} = q + (-p) = q - p$.

(d) $\vec{CA} = \vec{CB} + \vec{BA} = -p - q$, because $\vec{CB}$ is parallel but in the opposite direction to $\vec{EF}$ and $\vec{BA}$ is parallel but in the opposite direction to $\vec{ED}$.

a

1.

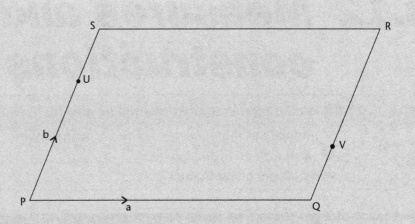

PQRS is a parallelogram; $\overrightarrow{PQ} = \boldsymbol{a}$ and $\overrightarrow{PS} = \boldsymbol{b}$.

U is a point such that PU : US = 2 : 1 and V is a point such that RV : VQ = 2 : 1.

Find (a) $\overrightarrow{RS}$ (b) $\overrightarrow{QS}$ (c) $\overrightarrow{SU}$ (d) $\overrightarrow{UV}$.

1. (a) $-\boldsymbol{a}$ (b) $\boldsymbol{b} - \boldsymbol{a}$

(c) $-\dfrac{1}{3}\boldsymbol{b}$

(d) $\dfrac{1}{3}\boldsymbol{b} + \boldsymbol{a} - \dfrac{2}{3}\boldsymbol{b} = \boldsymbol{a} - \dfrac{1}{3}\boldsymbol{b}$

3.12 Measures and constructions

LEARNING SUMMARY

After studying this section, you will be able to:

● **understand that measurements are approximate**
● **work with compound units**
● **do simple constructions**

Upper and lower bounds

All measurements are approximations. Measurements are given to the nearest practical unit. Measuring a value to the nearest unit means deciding that it is nearer to one mark on a scale than another; in other words it is within half a unit of that mark.

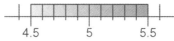

4.5   5   5.5

Anything within the shaded area is 5 to the nearest unit. The boundaries for this interval are 4.5 and 5.5 and this would be written as $4.5 \leqslant$ measurement < 5.5. where 4.5 is the lower bound and 5.5 is the upper bound.

Examples

(a) Tom won the 100 m race with a time of 12.2 seconds, to the nearest tenth of a second. What are the upper and lower bounds for this time?

The lower bound = 12.15 sec and the upper bound = 12.25 sec.

(b) A mass, given as 46 kg to the nearest kg, lies between what limits?
The mass is between 45.5 kg and 46.5 kg.

Compound units

Some measures depend upon other measures, for example:

$$\text{average speed} = \frac{\text{total distance travelled}}{\text{total time taken}}, \text{ and density} = \frac{\text{mass}}{\text{volume}}.$$

Examples

(a) Find the average speed of a car which travelled 150 miles in two and a half hours.

$$\text{average speed} = \frac{150}{2.5} = 60 \text{ mph}$$

(b) Calculate the density of a rock of mass 780 g and volume 84 cm^3. Give the answer to a suitable degree of accuracy.

$$\text{density} = \frac{780}{84} = 9.28571 \text{ g cm}^{-3} = 9 \text{ g cm}^{-3}$$

Constructions

You need to be able to complete various constructions. Remember it is often helpful to make a sketch diagram first.

Triangles

The standard constructions for triangles were outlined Section 3.1 where the properties of congruent triangles were discussed.

The perpendicular bisector of a line

To bisect line AB:

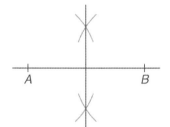

- using a pair of compasses, with centres A and B, draw arcs with the same radius to intersect either side of line AB
- join the points of intersection: this line is the perpendicular bisector of AB.

The perpendicular from a point to a line

To draw the perpendicular from P to a given line:

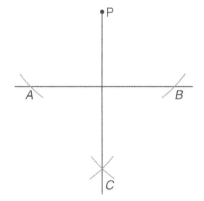

- from P draw arcs to cut the line at A and B
- from A and B draw arcs with the same radius to intersect at C
- join P to C: this line is perpendicular to the line AB.

To bisect an angle

To bisect the angle at A:

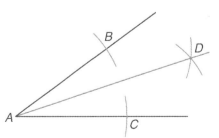

- with centre A draw arcs to cut the lines at B and C
- with the same radius draw arcs centre B and C to cut at D
- join A to D.

PROGRESS CHECK

1 Complete the sentences:
   (a) A height given as 5.7 m to two significant figures is between ___ m and ___ m.
   (b) A volume given as 568 ml, to the nearest millilitre, is between ___ ml and ___ ml.
   (c) A winning time given as 23.93 s to the nearest hundredth of a second is between ___ s and ___ s.

2 A car travels 20 km in 12 minutes. What is the average speed in km/h?

3 Calculate the density of a stone of mass 350 g and volume 45 cm^3.

3 7.7 g cm^{-3}
2 100 km/h
(c) 23.925 s and 23.935 s
1 (a) 5.65 m and 5.75 m   (b) 567.5 ml and 568.5 ml

3.13 Mensuration

LEARNING SUMMARY

After studying this section, you will be able to:
- **find the volume and surface area of a sphere**
- **find the length of an arc**
- **find the area of a sector and a segment**

The sphere

KEY POINT

The volume of a sphere = $\dfrac{4}{3}\pi r^3$

The surface area of a sphere = $4\pi r^2$

You should have completed the work on volumes of 3D shapes in Section 3.7. Here are some further examples and questions to attempt.

Examples

(a) Find the volume and surface area of a sphere with a radius of 10 cm.

$$\text{Volume} = \frac{4}{3}\pi r^2$$

$$= \frac{4}{3} \times 3.142 \times 10^3$$

$$= 4189 \text{ cm}^3 \text{ (to the nearest whole number)}$$

$$\text{Surface area} = 4\pi r^2$$

$$= 4 \times 3.142 \times 10^2$$

$$= 1257 \text{ cm}^2 \text{ (to the nearest whole number)}$$

(b) A solid metal cone of height 20 cm and radius 12 cm is melted down to form a cylinder of the same height. What is the radius of the cylinder?

$$\text{Volume of cone} = \frac{1}{3}\pi r^2 h$$

$$= \frac{1}{3} \times \pi \times 12^2 \times 20$$

$$\text{Volume of cylinder} = \pi r^2 h$$

$$= \pi \times r^2 \times 20$$

$$\therefore \frac{1}{3} \times \pi \times 12^2 \times 20 = \pi \times r^2 \times 20$$

$$\therefore \qquad r^2 = \frac{1}{3} \times 12^2$$

$$\text{so} \qquad r^2 = 48$$

$$r = 6.9 \text{ cm}$$

Arcs, sectors and segments

Arcs

An **arc** is part of the circumference of a circle. The ends of an arc are formed by two radii as shown in the diagram.

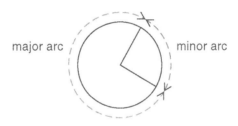

major arc ⋯ minor arc

The arc which subtends the larger angle at the centre is called the **major arc**, the arc which subtends the smaller angle at the centre is the **minor arc**.

The length of the arc depends on the size of the angle at the centre and on the radius of the circle. If the angle turned through to produce the arc is θ, then arc length $= \dfrac{\theta}{360} \times \pi d$ or $\dfrac{\theta}{360} \times 2\pi r$.

Example

Calculate the length of the minor arc of a circle with radius 6 cm if the angle formed at the centre is 75°.

$$\text{Length of arc} = \frac{\theta}{360} \times 2\pi r$$

$$= \frac{75}{360} \times 2 \times 3.142 \times 6$$

$$= 7.9 \text{ cm to 2 s.f.}$$

Sectors

A **sector** of a circle is an area bounded by two radii and an arc. A **minor sector** is formed by a minor arc, a **major sector** by a major arc.

In the same way as the arc length is a fraction of the circumference of a circle, the area of a sector is a fraction of the area of a circle.

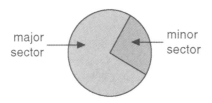

major sector

minor sector

> **KEY POINT**
>
> Area of sector $= \dfrac{\theta}{360} \times \pi r^2$

Example

Calculate the area of the sector of a circle with subtended angle 70° and radius 10 cm.

$$\text{Area of sector} = \frac{\theta}{360} \times \pi r^2$$

$$= \frac{70}{360} \times 3.142 \times 10^2$$

$$= 61.1 \text{ cm}^2$$

Segments

A **segment** of a circle is the area bounded by a chord and an arc.

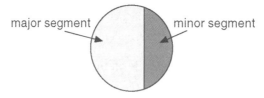

major segment

minor segment

To work out the area of a minor segment first work out the area of the sector, *AOBC*, and then subtract the area of the triangle *AOB* formed by the chord and the two radii.

For the major segment, the area is found by calculating the area of the major sector, *AOBD*, and adding the area of the triangle *AOB*.

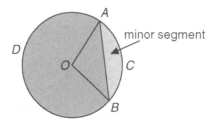

minor segment

Example

To help prevent liquid spillages from spreading, a barrier is made from a rubber compound.

The cross-section of the barrier is as shown below. It is made from a circular tube, of radius 20 cm, with a flat base. Calculate the volume of rubber needed for a 10 m length of tubing.

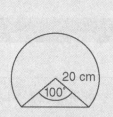

$$\text{Area of major sector} = \frac{260}{360} \times \pi \times 20^2$$

Using the formula
$A = \dfrac{1}{2} ab \sin C$

$$= 907.56 \text{ cm}^2$$

$$\text{Area of triangle} = \frac{1}{2} \times 20 \times 20 \times \sin 100$$

$$= 197 \text{ cm}^2$$

$$\text{Total cross-sectional area} = 1104.6 \text{ cm}^2$$

$$\therefore \quad \text{Volume} = 10 \times 100 \times 1104.6 \text{ cm}^3$$

1 m³ = 10⁶ cm³

$$= 1\,104\,600 \text{ cm}^3 = 1.1 \text{ m}^3$$

PROGRESS CHECK

1 A child's toy is made from a cylinder, of radius 3 cm and height 3 cm with a hemisphere fixed to the top, as shown.
Find the volume of the toy.

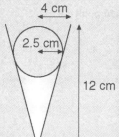

2 The sketch shows an ice-cream cone of radius 4 cm and depth 12 cm in which there is a sphere of ice cream of radius 2.5 cm. The ice cream melts and runs into the base of the cone. Find the depth of the liquid ice cream when this has happened.

3 Find the shaded area in the following diagram:

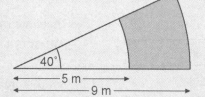

4 The chord *AB* subtends an angle of 130° at the centre, *O*, of a circle.
The diameter of the circle is 16 cm.
Find the area of the minor segment, which is shaded in the diagram.

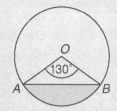

4 48.1 cm²
3 19.5 m²
2 8.25 cm
1 141 cm³ to the nearest whole number

3.14 Loci

LEARNING SUMMARY

After studying this section, you will be able to:

● *construct a locus which fulfils specified conditions*

Three important loci

KEY POINT The locus of a point is the path traced out by a point when it obeys certain constraints, or conditions.

For instance, the locus of a point which moves so that its path is always at the same distance from a fixed point is as follows:

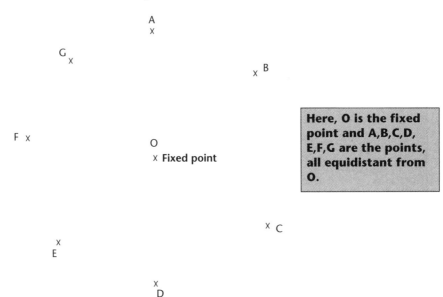

Here, O is the fixed point and A,B,C,D, E,F,G are the points, all equidistant from O.

There are many more such points – in fact an infinite number of them, and the path they form (or the shape they make) is a circle around O.

Another important locus is that formed by the points which are equidistant from two given points.
Here, P and Q are two given fixed points.
Clearly A – the mid-point of P and Q, satisfies the condition as B, C and D.
A,B,C and D lie along the **perpendicular bisector** of PQ.

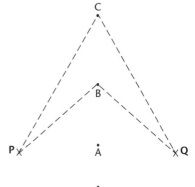

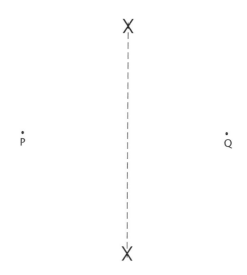

Reminder:
To bisect PQ, place a compass point at P and swing arcs above and below the line formed by joining P and Q. With the same compass length, repeat the process at Q. The line joining the two points of the intersection of the arcs is the perpendicular bisector.

A third important locus is the one is equidistant from two lines.

(a) If the two given lines are parallel, then the locus is also parallel to them and mid-way between them.

A ─────────────────────

B ─────────────────────

Required locus – the 'dotted line' in the middle of the road.

(b) If the two lines intersect, then the locus lies along the line that bisects the angle between them.

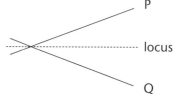

Reminder:
To bisect an angle, place a compass at O and make an arc to cut each of the rays at A and B respectively. Then place a compass at A and swing an arc in the central portion; without changing the compass length, repeat the process at B to find point Y. Then, OY is the angle bisector.

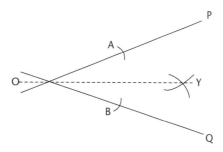

Example

Sachin finds a treasure map. It gives the following instructions:

'Captain Blackbeard's treasure is at the same distance from Spyglass Hill, as it is from Lookout Mountain. It is 2 km from Skeleton Tree.

(a) Using a scale of 0.5 cm: 1 km, locate the position of the treasure on the map.

(b) How far is the treasure from Dead Man's Cave?

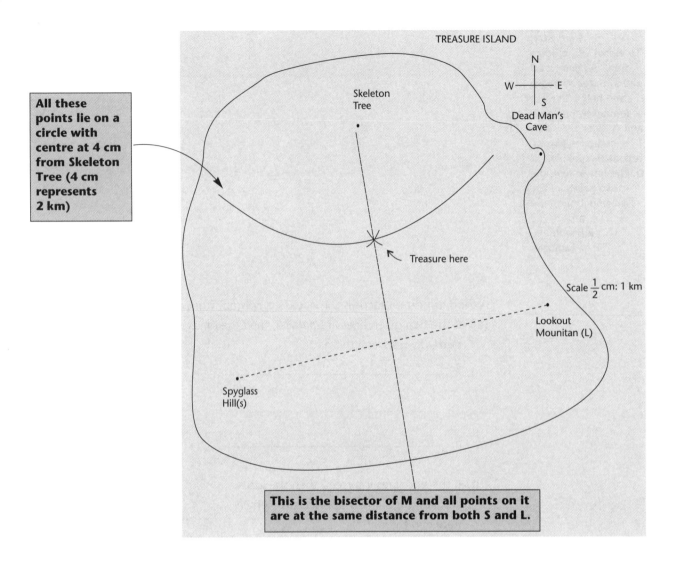

All these points lie on a circle with centre at 4 cm from Skeleton Tree (4 cm represents 2 km)

TREASURE ISLAND

Skeleton Tree

Dead Man's Cave

Treasure here

Scale $\frac{1}{2}$ cm: 1 km

Lookout Mounitan (L)

Spyglass Hill(s)

This is the bisector of M and all points on it are at the same distance from both S and L.

(b) Also, distance from treasure to Dead Man's Cave is 7 cm which implies
7 × 2 km = 14 km.

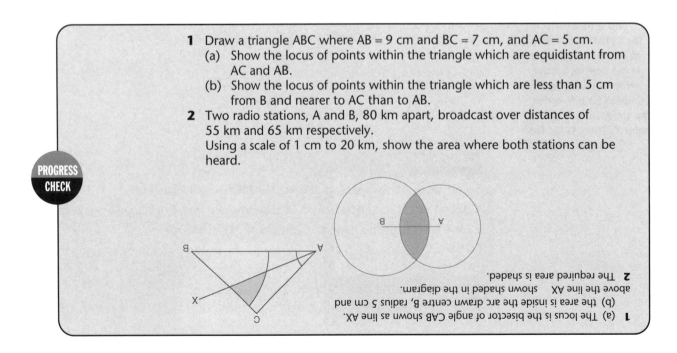

PROGRESS CHECK

1 Draw a triangle ABC where AB = 9 cm and BC = 7 cm, and AC = 5 cm.
 (a) Show the locus of points within the triangle which are equidistant from AC and AB.
 (b) Show the locus of points within the triangle which are less than 5 cm from B and nearer to AC than to AB.
2 Two radio stations, A and B, 80 km apart, broadcast over distances of 55 km and 65 km respectively.
 Using a scale of 1 cm to 20 km, show the area where both stations can be heard.

2 The required area is shaded.
1 (a) The locus is the bisector of angle CAB shown as line AX.
 (b) the area is inside the arc drawn centre B, radius 5 cm and above the line AX shown shaded in the diagram.

Sample IGCSE questions

1 This coil of piping has 15 turns.
The diameter of the coil is about 3 m.

(a) Estimate the length of the pipe. [2]

(b) This is the cross-section of the pipe.

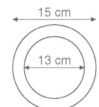

A one-metre length has mass 0.89 kg.
Calculate the density of the material.
State the units of your answer. [7]

This is an example of a multistep question. You are not asked specifically to find the volume but this is a necessary step towards finding the density.

(a) $\pi \times 3 \times 15$ ✔
    $\approx 140\ m$ (or 135 m)   ✔

(b)   Area of cross-section $= \pi(7.5^2 - 6.5^2)cm^2$ ✔✔
    Volume of 1-metre length $= 100\pi(7.5^2 - 6.5^2)\ cm^3$ ✔

$$= \frac{\pi(7.5^2 - 6.5^2)}{10\,000}\ m^3$$ ✔

$$= 0.0044\ m^3$$

Divide by 1 000 000 to change cm^3 to m^3.

$$Density = \frac{mass}{volume}$$ ✔

You have to state the units. You could give the answer in g/cm^3. This is the given answer divided by 1000.

$$= \frac{0.89}{0.0044} = 202.3\ kg/m^3$$ ✔✔

2 $ABCD$ is an isosceles trapezium. Angle $ACD = x°$.

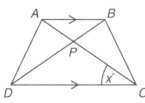

(a) Find the size of:
(i) angle ABD
(ii) angle APD
giving your reasons. [3]

(b) Prove that $ABCD$ is a cyclic quadrilateral [4]

Sample IGCSE questions

This is a straightforward question designed to test your ability to reason geometrically and your knowledge of angle facts etc.

It may help to mark on the diagram the facts you are given and the values that you calculate as you work towards the solution.

(a) (i) Because ABCD is isosceles, triangle ABP is isosceles therefore
angle ABD = angle BAC ✔
angle BAC = angle BCD = x (alternate angles) ✔
therefore angle ABD = x

(ii) Also triangle DPC is isosceles, therefore angle APD = 2x
(exterior angle of triangle) ✔

(b) Angle DAB = angle ABC (symmetry) ✔
angle ABC + angle BCD = 180° (AB||DC) ✔
∴ angle DAB + angle BCD = 180° ✔
∴ ABCD is a cyclic quadrilateral (opposite angles add to 180°) ✔

3 The diagram shows a closed tank used to mix ice-cream.

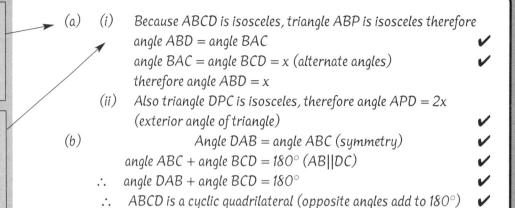

3 m

1.4 m

The tank is in the form of a cylinder of height 3 m fixed on top of a hemisphere of radius 1.4 m.

(a) Calculate, to the nearest square metre, the total surface area of the tank. **[4]**

The tank contains ice cream to a level 30 cm below the top.

(b) Calculate, in cubic metres, correct to one decimal place, the volume of ice cream in the tank. **[4]**

The ice cream is poured into tubs. The tubs are in the form of a cone of height $(h + 7)$ cm, diameter 8 cm with a cone of height h cm and diameter 6 cm removed.

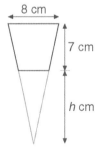

8 cm

7 cm

h cm

(c) (i) Using similar triangles, calculate the height h. **[3]**

(ii) Calculate the number of tubs which can be filled with ice-cream from the tank using your answer from part (b). **[4]**

Sample IGCSE questions

Remember to divide the area and volume formula for a sphere by 2 in this question.

Your answers may differ slightly depending on the value of π used.

Although your answers are rounded use unrounded values in subsequent calculations.

(a) Surface area $= \pi r^2 + 2\pi rh + 2\pi r^2$ ✔

$= \pi \times 1.4^2 + 2 \times \pi \times 1.4 \times 3 + 2 \times \pi \times 1.4^2$

$= 6.158 + 26.393 + 12.317$ ✔

$= 44.87\,m^2$ ✔

$= 45\,m^2$ ✔

(b) $3 - 0.3 = 2.7$ ✔

Volume $= \pi \times 1.4^2 \times 2.7 + \dfrac{1}{2} \times \dfrac{4\pi}{3} \times 1.4^3$ ✔

$= 16.63 + 5.75$ ✔

$= 22.38 = 22.4\,m^3$ to 1 d.p. ✔

(c) (i) $\dfrac{h}{h+7} = \dfrac{3}{4}$ ✔

$\therefore \quad 4h = 3h + 21$ ✔

$\therefore \quad h = 21$ ✔

(ii) Volume of tub $= \dfrac{1}{3} \times \pi \times 4^2 \times (21+7) - \dfrac{1}{3} \times \pi \times 3^2 \times 21$

✔

$= \dfrac{1}{3} \times \pi \,(16 \times 28 - 9 \times 21)$ ✔

$= 271.26\,cm^3$ ✔

$\therefore \quad$ number of tubs $= \dfrac{22.38 \times 1\,000\,000}{271.26}$

$= 82503.9 = 82\,500$ to the nearest hundred

✔

4 The shaded segment of the diagram shows the shape of the interior window ledge of a large bay window for a shop.

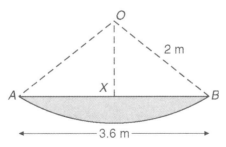

The straight edge AB is 3.6 m long and the curved edge AB is an arc of a circle of radius 2 m.

The window ledge is to be covered with a sheet of plastic with a length of beading curved along the arc AB.

(a) Calculate:
   (i) the angle AOB [3]
   (ii) the length of beading. [3]
(b) Calculate the area of the window ledge. [8]

Sample IGCSE questions

(a)   (i) $\sin XOB = \dfrac{1.8}{2}$ ✔

           angle $XOB = 64.16$ ✔

           angle $AOB = 128.3$ ✔

   (ii)   length of arc $= \dfrac{128.3}{360} \times 2 \times \pi \times 2$ ✔✔

                    $= 4.48$ m   ✔

(b)   area of sector $= \dfrac{128.3}{360} \times \pi \times 2^2$ ✔

                    $= 4.48$ m^2 ✔

                $OX = \sqrt{2^2 - 1.8^2}$ ✔

                    $= 0.87$ m   ✔

   area of triangle $OAB = \dfrac{1}{2} \times 3.6 \times 0.87$ ✔

                    $= 1.57$ m^2 ✔

       area of ledge $= 4.48 - 1.57$

                    $= 2.91$ m^2 ✔

                    $= 2.9$ m^2 (to 1 d.p.)   ✔

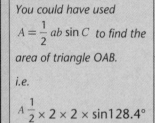

You could have used $A = \dfrac{1}{2} ab \sin C$ to find the area of triangle OAB.

i.e.

$A \dfrac{1}{2} \times 2 \times 2 \times \sin 128.4°$

---

5   ABCD is a parallelogram. M is the mid-point of DC.

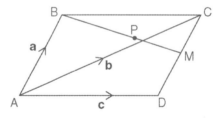

(a)   Find $\overrightarrow{DC}, \overrightarrow{DM}, \overrightarrow{AM}$ in terms of **b** and **c**.   **[3]**

(b)   Find $\overrightarrow{BM}$ in terms of **a**, **b** and **c**.   **[2]**

P is a point on BM such that $\overrightarrow{BP} = \dfrac{2}{3} \overrightarrow{BM}$.

(c)   Express $\overrightarrow{BP}$ in terms of **a** and show that $\overrightarrow{AP}$ can be expressed in the form $\dfrac{1}{n}(\mathbf{a} + \mathbf{b} + \mathbf{c})$ where **n** is an integer.   **[5]**

(d)   Use the fact that **b** = **a** + **c** to find $\overrightarrow{AP}$ in terms of **b** only. What can you deduce about the position of P?   **[3]**

Sample IGCSE questions

Make sure you check the directions of the vectors you are using.

(a) $\overrightarrow{DC} = \overrightarrow{DA} + \overrightarrow{AC} = -\mathbf{c} + \mathbf{b}$ ✔

$\overrightarrow{DM} = \frac{1}{2}\overrightarrow{DM} = \frac{1}{2}(-\mathbf{c} + \mathbf{b})$ ✔

$\overrightarrow{AM} = \overrightarrow{AD} + \overrightarrow{DM} = \mathbf{c} + \frac{1}{2}(-\mathbf{c} + \mathbf{b}) = \frac{1}{2}(\mathbf{c} + \mathbf{b})$ ✔

(b) $\overrightarrow{BM} = \overrightarrow{BA} + \overrightarrow{AM}$

There are alternative ways of reaching the solution i.e. in part (b) $\overrightarrow{BM}$ also equals $\overrightarrow{BC} + \overrightarrow{CM}$.

$= -\mathbf{a} + \frac{1}{2} + (\mathbf{c} + \mathbf{b})$ ✔

$= -\mathbf{a} + \frac{1}{2}\mathbf{c} + \frac{1}{2}\mathbf{b}$ ✔

(c) $\overrightarrow{BP} = \overrightarrow{BA} + \overrightarrow{AP}$

$= -\mathbf{a} + \overrightarrow{AP}$

$\therefore \overrightarrow{AP} = \overrightarrow{BP} + \mathbf{a}$ ✔

But $\overrightarrow{BP} = \frac{1}{2}\overrightarrow{BM}$

$= \frac{2}{3}\left(-\mathbf{a} + \frac{1}{2}\mathbf{c} + \frac{1}{2}\mathbf{b}\right)$ ✔

$\therefore \overrightarrow{AP} = -\frac{2}{3}\mathbf{a} + \frac{1}{3}\mathbf{b} + \frac{1}{3}\mathbf{c} + \mathbf{a}$ ✔

$= = \frac{1}{3}\mathbf{a} + \frac{1}{3}\mathbf{b} + \frac{1}{3}\mathbf{c} = \frac{1}{3}(\mathbf{a} + \mathbf{b} + \mathbf{c})$ ✔

$\therefore n = 3$ ✔

(d) $\overrightarrow{AP} = \frac{1}{3}(\mathbf{a} + \mathbf{b} + \mathbf{c}) = \frac{1}{3}[(\mathbf{a} + \mathbf{c}) + \mathbf{b}]$

$= \frac{2}{3}\mathbf{b}$ ✔

$= \frac{2}{3}\mathbf{b}$ ✔

Therefore P is on the line AC and $\frac{2}{3}$ of the way along it. ✔

Exam practice questions

1

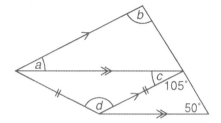

(a) Calculate the following angles:
  (i)   **b**   [1]
  (ii) **c**   [1]
  (iii) **a**   [1]
  (iv) **d**   [2]

(b) In the quadrilateral PQRS, X is the mid-point of QR, PX is parallel to SR and SX is parallel to PQ.

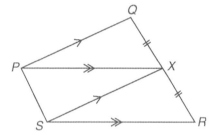

Prove that triangle PQX is congruent to triangle SXR.   [2]

2 A hemispherical bowl, radius r, is partially filled with water to a depth of $\frac{r}{2}$, as shown in the diagram.

Which of the following formulae could give the volume of water in the bowl?
Give a reason for your choice.

(a) $\dfrac{\pi r^2}{4}$ (b) $\dfrac{5\pi r^3}{24}$ (c) $\dfrac{\pi r^2}{4} + \dfrac{2\pi r^3}{3}$ (d) $\dfrac{3\pi r^4}{8}$ [2]

Exam practice questions

3 The diagram shows a quarter of a circle, with radius 17 cm and centre O.
Points A and X lie on the circumference of the circle. The point N lies on OX and angle ANO = 90°.
ON = 8 cm and AN = 15 cm.

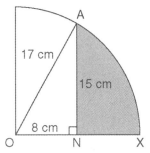

Find the shaded area on the diagram. **[5]**

4 In the diagram, OACB is a parallelogram. XY is parallel to OB. X is the mid-point of OA and N is the mid-point of XY.

$\overrightarrow{OA} = \mathbf{a}$ and $\overrightarrow{OB} = \mathbf{b}$

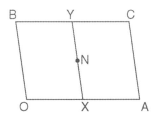

(a) Write, in terms of **a** and **b**:

$\overrightarrow{XN}, \overrightarrow{ON}, \overrightarrow{AN}, \overrightarrow{NB}$ **[3]**

(b) Deduce two facts about the points A, N, B. **[2]**

5 The diagram shows the position of three airports:
(A) Ayton, (B) Beesville and C (Colesville).

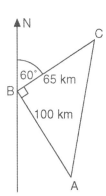

The distance from B to C is 65 km on a bearing of 060°,
angle CBA = 90° and AB = 100 km.

Exam practice questions

   (a)   Calculate, correct to three significant figures, the distance AC.   **[3]**

   (b)   Calculate, to the nearest degree, the bearing of A from C.   **[4]**

   (c)   An aircraft leaves B at 09.45 a.m. and flies directly to A arriving at 10.03 a.m. Calculate its average speed, giving your answer to an appropriate degree of accuracy.   **[4]**

6 The diagram shows a cone with height 8 cm and base radius 6 cm. The curved surface of the cone is made from a sector of a circle which is also shown.

 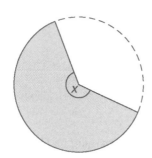

Find, leaving your answers as multiples of π:

   (a)   the area of the curved surface of the cone   **[3]**

   (b)   the volume of the cone   **[2]**

   (c)   the angle, x, made by the sector of the cone.   **[3]**

7 The diagram shows a square-based pyramid constructed to advertise a chocolate product. The sloping edge length is 21.2 cm and the side of the base is 7.4 cm long.

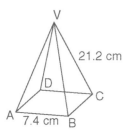

   (a)   Calculate the angle AVD.   **[4]**

   (b)   The height of the pyramid.   **[4]**

   (c)   The angle between edge VA and the base.   **[3]**

8 (a)   Sketch the curve $y = \cos x$ for values of x from 0 to 360°. Label the axes clearly.   **[2]**

   (b)   Write down the coordinates of the points of intersection with the x-axis.   **[2]**

Draw the line $y = 0.8$ on your sketch graph.

The x-coordinates of the points where the line meets the curve form the solution of an equation in x.

   (c)   Write down this equation.   **[1]**

   (d)   Solve the equation.   **[2]**

Overview

Topic	Section	Studied in class	Revised	Practice questions
4.1 Identification and selection	Key questions			
	Bias			
	Sampling			
	Primary and secondary data			
4.2 Collecting data	Questionnaires and surveys			
	Two-way tables			
4.3 Processing and representing data	Time series			
	Moving averages			
	Scatter diagrams			
	Stem and leaf tables			
	Cumulative frequency			
	Quartiles			
	Histograms			
	Box and whisker plots			
	Finding the mean, median and mode of grouped data			
4.4 Probability	Independent events			
	Mutually exclusive events			
	Tree diagrams			
	Probability of non-occurence of an event			
4.5 Interpretation	Comparing data			

4.1 Identification and selection

LEARNING SUMMARY

After studying this section, you will be able to:

- *identify key questions to be asked and how to ask them*
- *recognise bias*
- *understand sampling and use sampling techniques*
- *distinguish between primary and secondary data*

Key questions

As you will know from work completed earlier in your school life, handling data is concerned with the analysis and interpretation of data. The data is often collected in response to questions asked. As part of your coursework you will have to complete, or you may already have completed, a data handling task. This task may have involved the forming of a hypothesis. In order to do this, you must ask questions and on the written examination papers you may be asked to make comments on the quality and appropriateness of questions to be asked as part of a survey.

Here are some 'issues' and some questions you might choose to ask:

(a) travel to school

   (i)   How long does it take you?

   (ii)   How far away from school do you live?

   (iii) How do you travel to school?

(b) holiday destinations

   (i)   Do you like to go somewhere hot?

   (ii)   When do you go?

   (iii) Do you like 'activity holidays'?

You might like to think of some more questions that it would be appropriate to ask for either of these issues.

However you must remember that the answers to the questions asked have to be analysed.

KEY POINT

Those questions where the answer will be '*yes*' or '*no*' are clearly easy to analyse. Those where responses can be '*qualified*' such as '*do you eat breakfast?*' — answer '*sometimes*' and questions with an '*or*' statement in them, for example '*Do you eat meat or vegetables?*' should be avoided.

Bias

In data handling, the word **population** is used for a collection, set or group of objects being studied.

Anything that distorts data so that it will not give a fairly representative picture of a population is called **bias**.

Two common ways in which bias arises are:

(a) through the style of the questions asked, e.g. asking a leading question such as *'Normal people watch the news on TV. Do you watch the news?'* and (b) from the population asked.

One way to avoid bias is by selecting an appropriate sample so that the results obtained represent the whole population. The size of a sample is important: it should be large enough to represent the population but small enough to be manageable.

Two examples of biased samples are:

(a) investigating the pattern of absence from a school by studying the registers in December. [This might be biased because (i) students are more likely to be ill in the winter months compared with, say, the summer months. (ii) Older students might be absent for interviews. (iii) The pattern of any truancy might vary.]

(b) finding out opinions about school dinners by asking the first 20 students in Year 11 seen in the dinner queue one day. [This might be biased because (i) only those eating school dinners might be asked – those eating sandwiches because they don't like school dinners might not be asked. (ii) The opinions of pupils in other years won't be recorded.]

Sampling

A **sample** is a small part of a population. Samples are used because it is quicker and cheaper to sample a population rather than to collect information from the whole population. Conclusions drawn from the samples can then be applied to the whole population.

If the structure or composition of the population is known then it is important to ensure that the sample (or samples) represents that population and thus any variations in the population should be reflected in the sample, which is therefore a representative sample.

Sampling methods

1 Systematic sampling

An example of this method is the selection of a 10% sample by going through the population picking every tenth item or individual. The drawback is that this only provides a representative sample if the population is arranged in a random way and not in a way that might introduce bias, for example, if high or low values are grouped together.

> **Always show/state the type of sampling you are using and why.**

2 Attribute sampling

In this method, the selection of the sample is made by choosing some attribute which is totally unrelated to the variable being investigated. For example, choosing a sample to investigate any relationship between head size and height from a list of people on the basis of their birthday being the first of the month.

3 Stratified sampling

The population is divided into strata or sub-groups and the sample chosen to reflect the properties of these sub-groups. For example, if the population contained three times as many people under 25 as over 25 then the sample should also contain three times as many people under 25. The sample should also be large enough for the results to be significant.

4 Random sampling

In random sampling, every member of a population has an equal chance of being selected. The sample could be chosen by giving every member of the population a number and using random number tables, or the random number function on your calculator, to select the sample. To ensure a sample is random and as accurate as possible, ideally the sampling should always be repeated a number of times and the results averaged.

5 Quota sampling

This method is often used in market research where people interviewed have to be of a certain age, sex or social class etc.

6 Cluster sampling

The population is divided into small groups called clusters. One or more clusters are chosen using random sampling. This can lead to bias if the clusters are all different.

7 Stratified random sampling

A stratified random sample is obtained by:

- separating the population into appropriate categories or strata, e.g. by age,
- finding out what proportion of the population is in each stratum,
- selecting a sample from each stratum in proportion to the stratum size.

This can be done by random sampling hence the technique is known as stratified random sampling.

Example

A survey about sport is carried out among students in Years 9, 10 and 11. There are 210 students in Year 9, 225 in Year 10 and 195 in Year 11. A sample of 50 students is taken.

The sample size from each of the three year groups must be in proportion to the stratum size so the 50 students are selected as follows:

There are 210 + 225 + 195 = 630 students in total.

Year	Fraction of students	Number of students in the sample of 50	
9	$\dfrac{210}{630}$	$\dfrac{210}{630} \times 50 = 17$	**Round to the nearest integer.**
10	$\dfrac{225}{630}$	$\dfrac{225}{630} \times 50 = 18$	
11	$\dfrac{195}{630}$	$\dfrac{195}{630} \times 50 = 15$	

Select 17 students from Year 9, 18 from Year 10 and 15 from Year 11 at random.

A different form of sampling is illustrated by this example.

Example

The natterjack toad is an increasingly threatened species.

Scientists want to find out how many of the toads live in and around a pond.

To do this they catch 20 natterjack toads and mark them in a harmless way.

The toads are then released.

Next day another 20 are caught. 5 of these toads have already been marked, in other words 25% (5 out of a sample of 20) are already marked.

But 20 toads were marked initially.

This suggests that 25% of the population is about 20.

$$\frac{25}{100} \times P = 20$$

$$\therefore P = 80$$

Therefore, the total population is 80.

Primary and secondary data

Primary data are data collected by the person who is going to analyse and use it. **Secondary data** are data that are available from an external source such as books, newspapers, or the internet.

Example

Which of the following are primary and which secondary data?

(a) Looking at records to see how many babies were born each day in December.

(b) Measuring the length of pebbles in a sample of pebbles from the beach.

(c) Counting the number of red cars passing the school gate.

(d) Phoning local shops, supermarkets, garages etc to find out how much the pay for a Saturday job is.

(e) Looking at the top ten charts to see which group is top each week.

(f) Finding out information for a holiday by looking at brochures.

(a) secondary   (b) primary   (c) primary   (d) primary

(e) secondary   (f) secondary

> **KEY POINT**   Try to start with enough primary or secondary data that will allow you to sample from it.

PROGRESS CHECK

1 Why might this method give a biased sample?
An engineer is carrying out a traffic survey to find out how busy a particular road is. He counts the number of cars which pass a point on two days between 2 p.m. and 3 p.m.

PROGRESS
CHECK

2 For each of the following, write down which sampling method is being used to carry out a survey of pupils in Years 10 and 11 in a school.
   (a) Listing all the pupils in Year 10 and Year 11 in alphabetical order, then choosing the first and every fifth pupil after that.
   (b) Numbering all the tutor groups from 1 to 10. Writing the numbers 1 to 10 on slips of paper and putting them into a bag which is shaken. One slip is taken out and the number on this slip gives the tutor group.
   (c) Choosing the first 10 boys and the first 10 girls from the year groups who are in the dinner queue.
   (d) Listing all the students in Year 10 and Year 11 and giving each a number and using random numbers to select the sample.
   (e) There are 150 pupils in Year 10 and 165 pupils in Year 11. The sample contains 10 pupils from Year 10 and 11 from Year 11 chosen at random.

3 The table shows the numbers of boys and girls in Year 10 and Year 11 of a school.

	Year 10	Year 11
Boys	115	128
Girls	110	115

The headteacher wants to find out their views about changes to the school uniform and takes a stratified random sample of 40 pupils from Year 10 and Year 11.
Calculate the number of pupils to be sampled from Year 11.

3 Year 11 $= \frac{243}{468} \times 40 = 21$ (to nr. whole number)

2 (a) systematic (b) cluster (c) quota (d) random (e) stratified random

1 It may be biased because:
(a) the time is not appropriate – doesn't consider the rush hour for example (b) the length of time for the survey, 1 hour, is not sufficient (c) two days doesn't allow for variations i.e. could be Saturday, could be a holiday, could be market day . . .

4.2 Collecting data

LEARNING
SUMMARY

After studying this section, you will be able to:

● *write and use questionnaires*
● *make and use two-way tables*

Questionnaires and surveys

There are some standard ways of gathering information and data:

1 By questionnaire
   ● A questionnaire should give sufficient choices to cover the possible answers.
   ● The information must not be ambiguous.
   ● Answers should be short and capable of being analysed simply — yes/no types of responses are clearly the best.
   ● Questions should not be biased and should be short and easily understood.
   ● Questions should be relevant to the survey.

2 By observation

Here you need to consider:

- whether you are actually answering the question asked
- does the time and place of the observation matter?
- did you collect data for long enough?

3 By experiment

Questions to ask here include:

- does the experiment test the concept or hypothesis?
- have you carried out sufficient experiments producing enough results to reflect what is happening?

Questionnaire design

The best way to learn to write appropriate questions is to look at some good examples and some poor examples, and look back at the notes on bias in Section 4.1.

Question	Comment
Normal students like pizza. Do you like pizza?	This is biased. The first sentence should not be there. It implies you aren't normal if you don't like pizza.
It is important to learn mathematics in school. Tick one box. ☐ Agree ☐ Disagree ☐ Don't know	This question is OK. It is clear and simple to analyse.
How old are you? ☐ 11–16 ☐ 16–18 ☐ 18–24	Where does a student aged 16 tick? The problem here is that the groups overlap, otherwise it would be a good question.

> Remember, tick boxes are easy to analyse

At the end of the survey you need to think about the presentation of your results. Decide whether to use scatter graphs, bar charts, histograms etc., which are discussed later, or two-way tables.

Two-way tables

These are used to show two sets of information.

> **Example**
> A teacher has conducted a survey of the students in Year 9 to find out their favourite language.
>
> | | French | German | Spanish | Total |
> |---|---|---|---|---|
> | Boys | 25 | 45 | 20 | 90 |
> | Girls | 50 | 43 | 53 | 146 |
> | Total | 75 | 88 | 73 | 236 |

This table shows that, 25 boys preferred French, 53 girls preferred Spanish, 88 students preferred German and so on.

Using tables like this will often allow you to find missing values.

Example

A group of 180 Year 7 and Year 8 students were asked if they preferred individual or team sports. 72 students out of a total of 96 Year 7 students said they preferred team sports and in total, 63 students preferred individual sports. The data is entered in a two-way table.

	Year 7	Year 8	Total
Individual sports			63
Team sports	72		
Total	96		180

The missing values can now be filled in giving:

	Year 7	Year 8	Total
Individual sports	24	39	63
Team sports	72	45	117
Total	96	84	180

1 A bookseller records the type of book men and women buy during one week. Copy and complete the table.

	Men	Women	Total
hardback fiction		32	88
paperback fiction	74		274
hardback non-fiction	83	24	
paperback non-fiction		120	
Total	313		

PROGRESS CHECK

1

	Men	Women	Total
hardback fiction	56	32	88
paperback fiction	74	200	274
hardback non-fiction	83	24	107
paperback non-fiction	100	120	220
Total	313	376	689

4.3 Processing and representing data

LEARNING SUMMARY

After studying this section, you will be able to:

- *recognise and interpret time series*
- *calculate moving averages*
- *plot scatter graphs*
- *construct and interpret stem and leaf tables*
- *draw and interpret cumulative frequency curves, histograms and box plots*
- *calculate the mean, median and mode for grouped data*

Time series

A time series is made up of numerical data recorded at intervals of time and plotted as a line graph. The diagram below shows some examples of time series:
Graph A shows random fluctuations.
Graph B shows regular fluctuations about the trend line: these are cyclical fluctuations.
Graph C shows seasonal fluctuations.

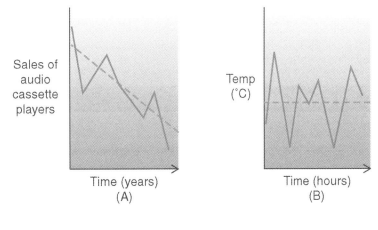

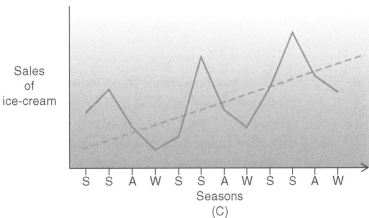

Example

The diagram below shows the number of people who book their holidays with Lumsden's Travel Service.

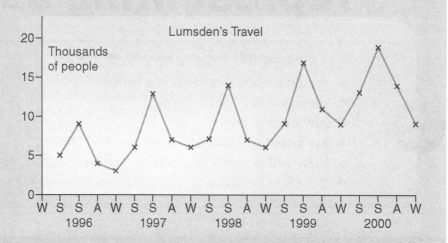

(a) How many people used the company in 1999?

(b) What was the percentage increase in people taking winter holidays between 1996 and 2000?

(a) 9000 + 17 000 + 11 000 + 9000 = 46 000

> Add up the Spring, Summer, Autumn and Winter numbers.

(b) $\dfrac{9000 - 3000}{3000} \times 100\% = 200\%$

> 9000 winter holidays in 2000, 3000 in 1996.

Moving averages

Moving averages are the averages worked out for a given number of data items, as you work through the data. A four-point moving average uses four data items in each calculation, a three-point moving average uses three and so on.

Example

Find the three-point moving average for the following data:

10, 11, 6, 17, 16, 9, 14

For the first three values, 10, 11, 6 the average is $(10 + 11 + 6) \div 3 = 9$.
Miss out the first value, 10, and include the next value, 17, giving the three numbers 11, 6, 17. The average is $(11 + 6 + 17) \div 3 = 11.3$.
Carry on through the data values until you reach the point where you include the last value. The complete list of averages, is:
$(10 + 11 + 6) \div 3 = 9$, $(11 + 6 + 17) \div 3 = 11.3$, $(6 + 17 + 16) \div 3 = 13$,
$(17 + 16 + 9) \div 3 = 14$, $(16 + 9 + 14) \div 3 = 13$.

Moving averages can help you to draw a trend line on a time-series graph.

Example

Look back at the Lumsden's Travel Service graph. Here is the table showing the values used to draw the graph. The values of four-point moving averages are added.

Year	Quarter	Number of people, in 1000s	Four-point moving average
1996	Spring	5	
	Summer	9	
			5.25
	Autumn	4	
			5.5
	Winter	3	
			6.5
1997	Spring	6	
			7.25
	Summer	13	
			8
	Autumn	7	
			8.25
	Winter	6	
			8.5
1998	Spring	7	
			8.5
	Summer	14	
			8.5
	Autumn	7	
			9
	Winter	6	
			9.75
1999	Spring	9	
			10.75
	Summer	17	
			11.5
	Autumn	11	
			12.5
	Winter	9	
			13
2000	Spring	13	
			13.75
	Summer	19	
			13.75
	Autumn	14	
	Winter	9	

> **These values should be lined up between adjacent seasons eg 5.25 should appear *between* Summer and Autumn etc.**

Plot these points on the graph and draw the trend line.

> **With data given in quarters like this, it is easy to plot the moving averages. After the first one they appear between the adjacent sections.**

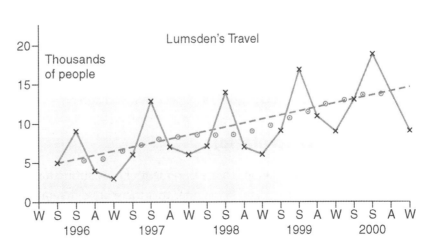

Lumsden's Travel

Scatter diagrams

Scatter diagrams, or scatter graphs, are used to see if there are any possible links or relationships between two features or variables. Values of the two features are plotted as points on a graph. If these points tend to lie in a straight line then there is a relationship or **correlation** between them.

Example

The table below shows the percentage marks gained in a history test and a geography test by the same 16 students.

History	73	58	62	53	40	61	63	46	48	49	60	61	61	69	85	48
Geography	67	58	52	53	45	57	48	49	53	53	55	58	59	54	62	57

This data is plotted on a scatter graph which suggests that there is a relationship between the results of the two subjects: the higher the history marks, the higher the geography marks. The mean marks for each subject are calculated: history 58.6, geography 55.0, which gives the 'mean point', which is plotted. A straight line is drawn through this mean point and the middle of the other points, as shown.

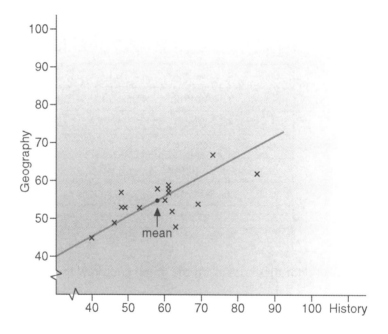

Draw lines across and up the graph to help.

A seventeenth student took the geography test but missed the history test. The geography score was 50%. The scatter graph can be used to estimate the history score: around 50%. Check that you agree.

Correlation

Correlation is a measurement of how strong a relationship there is between two sets of data. Remember that there are different kinds of correlation.

Positive correlation

In this example, as age increases so does height.

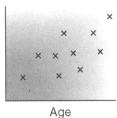

Height

Age

Negative correlation

In this example, the value decreases as the age increases.

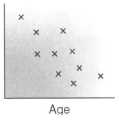

Value of car

Age

No correlation or zero correlation

In this example, there is no correlation between maths score and height.

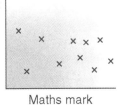

Height

Maths mark

Stem and leaf tables

A stem and leaf table shows the shape of a distribution. It is similar to a bar chart with the numbers in the distribution forming the bars.

> **Example**
> Here are the marks gained by 30 students in a mathematics examination.
>
> | | | | | | | | | | |
> |---|---|---|---|---|---|---|---|---|---|
> | 63 | 58 | 61 | 52 | 59 | 65 | 69 | 75 | 70 | 54 |
> | 57 | 63 | 76 | 81 | 64 | 68 | 59 | 40 | 65 | 74 |
> | 80 | 44 | 47 | 53 | 70 | 81 | 68 | 49 | 57 | 61 |
>
> The marks can be shown in a **stem and leaf** table like this:
> First: Divide each number into two parts: the tens and the units.
> Then write the tens figures in the left-hand column of a table.
> These are the 'stems'.
>
>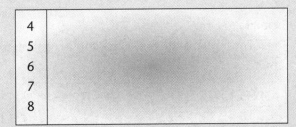
>
> 4
> 5
> 6
> 7
> 8
>
> Next go through the marks in turn and put in the units figure of each mark in the appropriate row. These are the 'leaves'.

Handling Data

the first value is 63		the next is 58		then 61	
4		4		4	
5		5	8	5	8
6	3	6	3	6	3 1
7		7		7	
8		8		8	

When all the marks are entered the table will look like this:

4	0 4 7 9
5	8 2 9 4 7 9 3 7
6	3 1 5 9 3 4 8 5 8 1
7	5 0 6 4 0
8	1 0 1

Finally rewrite the table so the units figures in each row are in size order, with the smallest first.

4	0 4 7 9
5	2 3 4 7 7 8 9 9
6	1 1 3 3 4 5 5 8 8 9
7	0 0 4 5 6
8	0 1 1

This is a finished stem and leaf table. It is a sort of frequency chart and allows you to read off certain information, for example:

- the modal group, the one with the highest frequency, is the 60–69 group
- there are 30 results so the median result is mid-way between the fifteenth and the sixteenth results. Starting at the first result, 40, and counting on 15 results gives 63; the sixteenth result is also 63, so the median result is 63.

 KEY POINT The stem is the first part of the number. The leaf has the end digits of the readings as in the example below.

Example

The following table gives the lengths, in centimetres, of 20 worms in a sample.

4.4	5.3	4.9	5.8	5.2	5.9	6.2	6.4	6.5	6.0
6.3	6.4	7.6	7.2	7.6	8.1	9.3	9.2	7.3	7.7

(a) Make a stem and leaf table to show the lengths.

(b) Use your table to find the median length.

(a) The completed stem and leaf table is:

```
4 | 4 9
5 | 2 3 8 9
6 | 0 2 3 4 4 5
7 | 2 3 6 6 7
8 | 1
9 | 2 3
```

(b) There are 20 values. The median will be mid-way between the tenth and the eleventh values. The tenth value is 6.4 and the eleventh value is 6.4 so the median is 6.4.

Cumulative frequency

In data handling, the frequency tells you how often a particular result was obtained. The **cumulative frequency** will tell you how often a result was obtained which was less than, $<$, or less than or equal to, $\leqslant$, a given or stated value in a collection of data.

The cumulative frequency is obtained by adding together the frequencies to give a 'running total'.

For, example, as part of a statistics project a student collected information on the numbers of brothers and sisters of children in Year 7. The results were recorded in a cumulative frequency table.

Number of brothers and sisters	Frequency	Cumulative frequency	
0	40	40	
1	53	93	← 93 = 40 + 53
2	37	130	← 130 = 93 + 37
3	13	143	← 143 = 130 + 13
4	6	149	← 149 = 143 + 6
5	1	150	← 150 = 149 + 1
6	1	151	← 151 = 150 + 1

> **Note how the cumulative frequency is calculated.**

The median is the value half-way through the data. The cumulative total is 151 so the median is the seventy-sixth value. At the end of the '0s' you have reached the fortieth value, at the end of the '1s' you have reached the ninety-third value so the seventy-sixth value must be 1, i.e. the median is 1.

If there are a lot of values they are best dealt with by treating them as grouped data.

Example

The table shows the marks gained in a test by the 60 pupils in a year group.

22	13	33	31	51	24	37	83	39	28
31	64	23	35	9	34	42	26	68	38
63	34	44	77	37	15	38	54	34	22
47	25	48	38	53	52	35	45	32	31
37	43	37	49	24	17	48	29	57	33
30	36	42	36	43	38	39	48	39	59

> **60 results are a lot to analyse so the results are grouped together in intervals.**

Put the marks in a grouped frequency table.

Mark, m	Frequency	Cumulative frequency
$0 \leqslant m < 10$	1	1
$10 \leqslant m < 20$	3	4
$20 \leqslant m < 30$	9	13
$30 \leqslant m < 40$	25	38
$40 \leqslant m < 50$	11	49
$50 \leqslant m < 60$	6	55
$60 \leqslant m < 70$	3	58
$70 \leqslant m < 80$	1	59
$80 \leqslant m < 90$	1	60

> **A sensible interval in this case is a band of 10 marks.**

The last column 'Cumulative frequency' gives the running total. Here the running total shows the number of pupils with less than a certain mark, for example, 38 pupils gained less than 40 marks.

The `values for cumulative frequency can be plotted to give a cumulative frequency curve as shown below:

> **Note that the cumulative frequency values are plotted at the upper value of each interval i.e. at 10, 20, 30 and so on because the intervals are based on discrete values i.e. marks.**

> **A cumulative frequency curve requires you to join the points with a curve. On a cumulative frequency graph you could join the points with straight lines.**

You can use a cumulative frequency curve to estimate the median. In this example there are 60 pupils so the median mark will be the thirtieth mark.

To find the median from the graph, find 30 on the vertical scale and go across the graph until you reach the curve and read off the value on the horizontal scale (look at the dotted line on the graph).

The median mark is about 37. Check that you agree.

Quartiles

As the name suggests quartiles are associated with quarters.

For the example on page 181, 'The numbers of brothers and sisters in Year 7', one-quarter of the way through the data is the thirty-eighth value (the median value ÷ 2) which is 0, the upper quartile is three-quarters of the way through the data, i.e. $3 \times 38 = 114$, the 114th value which is 2.
The interquartile range is the difference between the lower quartile value and the upper quartile value: in this case $2 - 0 = 2$

For the test marks example on page 182, the lower quartile is one-quarter of the way through the data and so is $60 \div 4$, or the fifteenth value. Drawing a line across the graph at 15 gives a mark of 31. The upper quartile is three-quarters of the way through the data and so is 3×15, or the forty-fifth value. Drawing a line across at 45 gives a mark of 45.

The interquartile range is the difference between the lower quartile value and the upper quartile value: in this case $45 - 31 = 14$.

Histograms

Histograms and bar charts are closely related.
- In a histogram the frequency of the data is shown by the **area** of each bar. (In a bar chart the frequency is shown by the **height** of each bar.)
- Histograms have bars, or columns, whose width is in proportion to the size of the group of data each bar represents, the class width, so the bars may have different widths. (In a bar chart the widths of each bar are usually the same.)
- The vertical scale is labelled 'frequency density'. (In a bar chart the vertical scale is the actual frequency.)
- Histograms can only be used to show continuous data which is numerical and grouped.

Example
A botanist measured the height of a type of plant growing in compost. The table shows the measurements.

Height, h cm	Frequency
$0 \leqslant h < 10$	22
$10 \leqslant h < 20$	35
$20 \leqslant h < 30$	38
$30 \leqslant h < 40$	28
$40 \leqslant h < 50$	13
$50 \leqslant h < 60$	9

Noltice use of '$\leqslant$' so, for example $20 \leqslant h < 30$ means all values between 20 and 30, including 20 but excluding 30.

because the widths of all the groups, the class widths, are the same the histogram can be drawn without any further calculation.

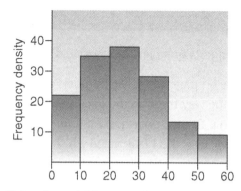

The vertical axis shows the frequency density. In this example it is frequency per 10 cm.

If the class widths are different then you must calculate the frequency densities as shown in the following example.

Example

A doctor investigated the ages of patients that visited her surgery over a period of time.

The table shows the findings.

Age, A, in years	Frequency
$0 \leqslant A < 20$	28
$20 \leqslant A < 30$	36
$30 \leqslant A < 40$	48
$40 \leqslant A < 50$	20
$50 \leqslant A < 70$	30
$70 \leqslant A < 100$	15

Here to draw the histogram you must first calculate the frequency densities:

Frequency density = frequency class ÷ class width

Class Age, A, in years	Frequency width	Frequency (f)	Frequency density
$0 \leqslant A < 20$	20	28	$28 \div 20 = 1.4$
$20 \leqslant A < 30$	10	36	$36 \div 10 = 3.6$
$30 \leqslant A < 40$	10	48	$48 \div 10 = 4.8$
$40 \leqslant A < 50$	10	20	$20 \div 10 = 2$
$50 \leqslant A < 70$	20	30	$30 \div 20 = 1.5$
$70 \leqslant A < 100$	30	15	$15 \div 30 = 0.5$

Note: frequency density = frequency per year

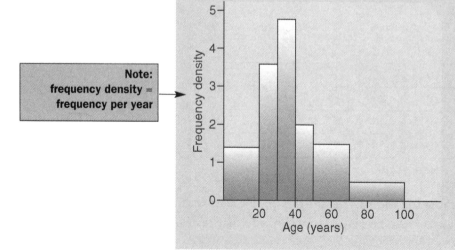

If the information is already given in a histogram it is possible to find out the frequencies and also estimate the mean.
This example shows how.

Example

A botanist measured the height of some bushes growing in a clay-type soil. The results are shown in this histogram.

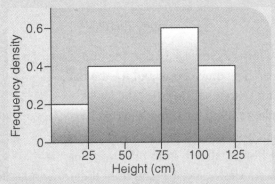

Find the number of bushes measured and estimate the mean height.

The frequency density = frequency ÷ column width.

The frequencies therefore are:
$0.2 \times 25 = 5$
$0.4 \times 50 = 20$
$0.6 \times 25 = 15$
$0.4 \times 25 = 10$

> **frequency = frequency density × column width**

The total frequency = 50

The mean can be estimated using the mid-point of each class width.

$\Sigma fx = (5 \times 12.5) + (20 \times 50) + (15 \times 87.5) + (10 \times 112.5) = 3500$

Therefore $\bar{x} = \dfrac{3500}{50} = 70$ i.e. the mean height = 70 cm

> **KEY POINT**
>
> **Histograms often have no label on the vertical axis. It is assumed that the scale is frequency density.**

Box and whisker plots

A box and whisker plot, sometimes just called a box plot, shows how the data is distributed. It can show the median, the quartiles and the range.

Example

A maths teacher recorded the times that a Year 7 class spent on their maths homework one night. The table shows the times, to the nearest minute, after they have been arranged in order, smallest to largest:

12	16	16	18	18	18	18	19	19	19
20	20	21	21	21	21	21	21	25	26
27	29	29	30	30					

The smallest value = 12, the largest = 30. The median is the thirteenth value = 21. The lower quartile is the median of that data to the left of the actual median:

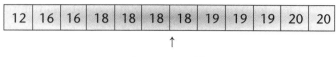

↑

lower quartile

The upper quartile is the median of that data to the right of the actual median:

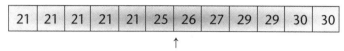

↑

upper quartile

so the lower quartile = 18 and the upper quartile = 25.5.
You can now draw a box plot for the data.
The 'box' stretches from 18, the lower
quartile, to 25.5, the upper quartile. The
median is shown inside the box at 21, and
the 'whiskers' stretch from the lower quartile
to the smallest value, 12, and from the upper quartile to the highest value, 30.

You can use a box plot to look at the shape of a distribution.

Symmetrical distribution
The median is in the centre.
The whiskers are of equal length.

Negative skew
The median is closer to the upper quartile.
The whiskers are of unequal length.

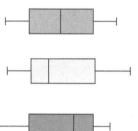

Positive skew
The median is closer to the lower quartile.
The whiskers are of unequal length.

Finding the mean, median and mode of grouped data

The mean, median and mode can be calculated from grouped data. This example shows how.

Example

Ann is completing a project comparing novels. She keeps a record of the number of words in each sentence in the first chapter of two novels. Here are her results for one novel.

number of words, w	frequency, f	cumulative frequency, cf	mid-value x	$f \times x$
1–5	16	16	3	$16 \times 3 = 48$
6–10	27	43	8	$27 \times 8 = 216$
11–15	28	71	13	$28 \times 13 = 364$
16–20	11	82	18	$11 \times 18 = 198$
21–25	12	94	23	$12 \times 23 = 276$
26–30	6	100	28	$6 \times 28 = 168$
31–35	5	105	33	$5 \times 33 = 165$
Totals	105			1435

Σf

Σfx

Modal class

Because the data is grouped the modal class is used instead of the mode. Here the **modal class** is 11–15 words as it has the highest frequency, 28.

Median

The median is estimated by 'interpolation'. There are 105 values so the middle value is the fifty-third value which will occur in the 11–15 group. This group is 5 numbers wide: 11, 12, 13, 14, 15. The frequency is 28 so this group has 28 values in it. The fifty-third value is the tenth of these 28 values because $53 = 43 + 10$, (the forty-third value is at the end of the 6–10 group) so an estimate would be $\frac{10}{28}$ of the way through this group.

So the median $= 11 + \frac{10}{28} \times 5$ giving 13 to the nearest whole number.

Mean

You cannot find the exact value of the mean when the data is grouped. You can estimate it by using the mid-value of each group. These are shown in the table as the x-values.

Multiply each x-value by the frequency, f, of the group, as shown in the last column of the table.

Add up the fx values to get Σfx.

Divide by the total frequency, Σf.

$$\text{Estimated mean} = \frac{\Sigma fx}{\Sigma f}$$

$$= \frac{1435}{105}$$

$$= 13.67$$

$$= 14 \text{ to the nearest whole number}$$

PROGRESS CHECK

1 The marks of 10 students in the two papers of a maths exam were:

Paper 1	20	32	40	45	60	67	71	80	85	91
Paper 2	15	25	40	40	50	60	64	75	76	84

Plot these marks on a scatter diagram.
A student scored 53 marks on paper 1. What would you estimate the likely mark to be on paper 2?

2 The table shows the length of time, in minutes, that customers queued at a supermarket checkout.

KEY POINT **Always explain why you are using mean, median or mode (modal class). Which is more appropriate depends on the context.**

Time, t min	Number of customers
$0 < t \leqslant 1$	4
$1 < t \leqslant 2$	12
$2 < t \leqslant 3$	22
$3 < t \leqslant 4$	37
$4 < t \leqslant 5$	47
$5 < t \leqslant 6$	33
$6 < t \leqslant 7$	30
$7 < t \leqslant 8$	12

(a) Draw a cumulative frequency curve for the data.
(b) Estimate the median time.
(c) Estimate the upper and lower quartiles and hence find the interquartile range.

3 A clothing manufacturer needs to know how long to make the sleeves of sweatshirts. 200 teenagers had their arm lengths measured. The results are shown in the table:

Arm length, L cm	Frequency, f
$40 \leqslant L < 45$	8
$45 \leqslant L < 50$	44
$50 \leqslant L < 55$	96
$55 \leqslant L < 60$	28
$60 \leqslant L < 70$	20
$70 \leqslant L < 80$	4

Draw a histogram to show this information.

4 This histogram shows the ages of people who live in a small village.

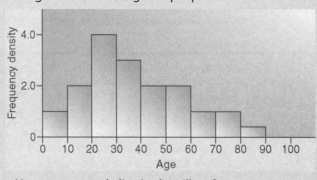

(a) How many people live in the village?
(b) Estimate their mean age.

5 John records how late his train is each working day over a 4-week period. These are the minutes late, to the nearest minute, for his journeys.

8	1	4	1	12	13	15	9	4	5
8	20	12	16	12	10	9	17	5	3

(a) Find the median.
(b) Find the upper and lower quartiles.
(c) Use these values to draw a box plot to show the times.

PROGRESS CHECK

6 The mathematics marks of 250 students have been recorded and are given in the table below. Copy and complete the table and estimate the mean and the median examination marks.

Mark range	Mid-value, x	Frequency, f	$f \times x$
0–9		3	
10–19		4	
20–29		6	
30–39		19	
40–49		40	
50–59		49	
60–69		52	
70–79		43	
80–89		25	
90–99		9	

7 Mary has kept a record of the money she spends on food for her family at the supermarket each month for the last 12 months.
  (a) Draw a graph to show this.

Month	Jan	Feb	Mar	Apr	May	Jun	Jul	Aug	Sept	Oct	Nov	Dec
Amount, £	193	198	194	200	197	203	198	199	201	202	203	210

  (b) Calculate a three point moving average for the data.
  (c) On your graph show the trend line.

PROGRESS CHECK

---

1 47 marks
2 From your graph the values should be close to these answers:
(b) median = 4.5 min, (c) the lower quartile = 3.4 min, the upper quartile = 5.8 min, the interquartile range = 2.4 min

3

Arm length, L cm	Frequency, x	class width	frequency density
$40 \leqslant L < 45$	8	5	$8 \div 5 = 1.6$
$45 \leqslant L < 50$	44	5	$44 \div 5 = 8.8$
$50 \leqslant L < 55$	96	5	$96 \div 5 = 19.2$
$55 \leqslant L < 60$	28	5	$28 \div 5 = 5.6$
$60 \leqslant L < 70$	20	10	$20 \div 10 = 2$
$70 \leqslant L < 80$	4	10	$4 \div 10 = 0.4$

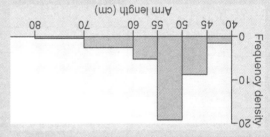

4 (a) total = 164 (b) mean age = 37.4 years
5 The box plot should show the following:
median = 9, lower quartile = 4.5, upper quartile = 12.5, interquartile range = 8, lower whisker = 1, upper whisker at 20
6 Estimated median = 60, estimated mean = 56 (both to the nearest whole number)
7 Moving averages are, in £:
195, 197.30, 197, 200, 199.30, 200.70, 202, 205

4.4 Probability

LEARNING SUMMARY

After studying this section, you will be able to:

- understand what independent and mutually exclusive events are
- use the multiplication rule for independent events
- use the addition rule for mutually exclusive events
- draw and use tree diagrams
- understand the relation between probabilities of occurence and non-occurence

Independent events

Two events are **independent** if the outcome of one event has no effect on the outcome of the other event. For example, rolling a dice and spinning a coin will be independent events because whatever is scored on the dice can have no effect on whether a head or a tail is obtained on the coin.

Example

Jodi is using a spinner and a dice. She spins the spinner and rolls the dice.

What is the probability that she will get red on the spinner and a score less than 4 on the dice?

You could draw a table showing all the possible outcomes. This is called a **possibility space** diagram.

		Dice					
		1	2	3	4	5	6
	Red, R	R,1	R,2	R,3	R,4	R,5	R,6
Spinner	Green, G	G,1	G,2	G,3	G,4	G,5	G,6
	Yellow, Y	Y,1	Y,2	Y,3	Y,4	Y,5	Y,6
	Blue, B	B,1	B,2	B,3	B,4	B,5	B,6

The possible ways of gaining a red and a score of less than 4 are shown highlighted in the table.

The probability of getting red and less than $4 = \frac{3}{24} = \frac{1}{8}$.

However because the events in the above example are independent, the probability can also be worked out using the **multiplication rule**.

If P(A) is the probability of gaining a red on the spinner, $P(A) = \frac{1}{4}$.

If P(B) is the probability of scoring less than 4 on the dice P(B) = $\frac{1}{2}$.

The probability of A and B happening is

The multiplication rule for independent events.

$$P(A \text{ and } B) = P(A) \times P(B) = \frac{1}{4} \times \frac{1}{2} = \frac{1}{8}$$

Mutually exclusive events

Events are **mutually exclusive** if they cannot happen at the same time. For example, if you roll a dice it is impossible to get a 3 at the same time as getting an even number.

For two mutually exclusive events, A and B, the probability that either event A or event B will occur is found by **adding** their probabilities together.

The addition rule for mutually exclusive events.

$$P(A \text{ or } B) = P(A) + P(B)$$

Thus for the dice example above, the probability of getting a 3 or getting an even number is

$$P(\text{getting a 3}) + P(\text{getting an even number}) = \frac{1}{6} + \frac{1}{2} = \frac{2}{3}$$

Example

Asif and Rakhi have designed a game for the school fair. In the game an ordinary dice is rolled twice. A prize is won if the total score on both dice is 6 or if the score on each dice is over 4. What is the probability of winning a prize?

List all the possible results in a table:

This is a possibility space diagram.

1,1	1,2	1,3	1,4	1,5	1,6
2,1	2,2	2,3	2,4	2,5	2,6
3,1	3,2	3,3	3,4	3,5	3,6
4,1	4,2	4,3	4,4	4,5	4,6
5,1	5,2	5,3	5,4	5,5	5,6
6,1	6,2	6,3	6,4	6,5	6,6

Here the possible ways of scoring 6 are shown in blue, and the possible ways of each score being more than 4 are shown in red.

If P(A) is the probability of a total score of 6 then

$$P(A) = \frac{5}{36}$$

If P(B) is the probability of each score being more than 4 then

$$P(B) = \frac{4}{36}$$

The probability of a total of 6 or of each score being more than 4, i.e. P(A **or** B) can be seen from the table as $\dfrac{9}{36}$, and

$$P(A) + P(B) = \dfrac{5}{36} + \dfrac{4}{36} = \dfrac{9}{36}.$$

Tree diagrams

Probability trees can be used to show the outcomes of two or more events. Each branch represents a possible outcome for an event. The probability of each outcome is written on the branch, the final result depends on the path taken through the tree.

Example

The probability that a new car will develop a fault in the first year is 0.85. Two new cars are chosen at random.

(a) Show all the possible outcomes on a tree diagram.

(b) Use the diagram to find the probability that both cars will develop a fault.

(c) Find the probability that only one car will develop a fault.

(a)
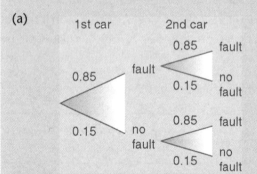

Remember that the sum of probabilities = 1. So if the probability of developing a fault = 0.85 the probability of not developing a fault = 0.15.

(b) The probability that both cars develop a fault = P(1st) × P(2nd)
$$= 0.85 \times 0.85$$
$$= 0.7225$$

(c) The probability that only one car develops a fault means either the first car **or** the second car has a fault.

P(1st fault) × P(2nd no fault) + P(1st no fault) × P(2nd fault)

= (0.85 × 0.15) + (0.15 × 0.85)

= 0.255

So the probability that only one car develops a fault is 0.255.

Example

A bag contains 7 red marbles and 4 white marbles. Two marbles are chosen without replacement (this means that the first marble is not put back in the bag before the second marble is chosen).

(a)   What is the probability that both marbles are red?

(b)   What is the probability that they are different colours?

(c)   What is the probability that both marbles are the same colour?

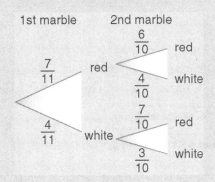

(a)   P (both red) = P(1st red and 2nd red) $= \dfrac{7}{11} \times \dfrac{6}{10} = \dfrac{21}{55}$

(b)   P (one red and one white) = P((1st red and 2nd white) or (1st white and 2nd red))

$$= \left(\dfrac{7}{11} \times \dfrac{4}{10} \right) + \left(\dfrac{4}{11} \times \dfrac{7}{10} \right)$$

$$= \dfrac{14}{55} + \dfrac{14}{55} = \dfrac{28}{55}$$

(c)   P (both the same) = P((1st red and 2nd red) or (1st white and 2nd white))

$$= \left(\dfrac{7}{11} \times \dfrac{6}{10} \right) + \left(\dfrac{4}{11} \times \dfrac{3}{10} \right)$$

$$= \dfrac{21}{55} + \dfrac{6}{55} = \dfrac{27}{55}$$

> **Note that the probability that both are the same = 1 – the probability that they are different**
> $$= 1 - \dfrac{28}{55}$$

PROGRESS CHECK

1   The probability that the school football team win their next match is 0.4. The probability that they draw their next match is 0.3. What is the probability that they win or draw their next match?

2   This spinner is used in a game. What is the probability that if it is spun twice you will get 'red' on both spins?

1   Mutually exclusive since win and draw cannot at the same time so
P(win or draw) = P(win) + P(draw) = 0.3 + 0.4 = 0.7
2   Independent events since second spin is not affected by first spin
P(red and red) = P(red) × P(red) = $\dfrac{1}{4} \times \dfrac{1}{4} = \dfrac{1}{16}$

Probability of non-occurrence of an event

A good shortcut in some questions is to remember that: the probability of something occurring, P(A) plus the probability of something not occurring, P($\overline{A}$) must equal 1.

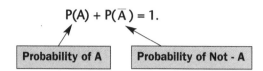

$$P(A) + P(\overline{A}) = 1.$$

| Probability of A | Probability of Not - A |

Example

If these are 3 green, 4 red, 5 yellow and 6 blue marbles in a bag, then: the probability of drawing a red marble out at random is:

| No. of red marbles |
| Total no. of marbles |
$$\frac{4}{18} = \frac{2}{9}$$

So the probability of drawing out a marble which is not red must be:

$$1 - \frac{2}{9} = \frac{7}{9}$$

We would, of course, had reached the same answer if we said:

$$P(not\text{-}red) = \frac{(green) + (yellow) + (blue)}{total\ number\ of\ marbles} = \frac{3 + 5 + 6}{18} = \frac{\overset{7}{\cancel{14}}}{\underset{9}{\cancel{18}}} = \frac{7}{9}.$$

The idea is particularly useful, when applied to probability trees.

Example

While driving to work, a woman passes two traffic lights. The probability that the first light is green is $\frac{3}{4}$ while the probability that the second light is green is $\frac{8}{15}$.

What is the probability that she is stopped by at least one light?

Ans: The probability that she is stopped by at least one light
= 1 – probability that she is stopped at no light
= 1 – probability that both lights are green

$$= 1 - \left(\frac{3}{4} \times \frac{8}{15}\right) = 1 - \frac{2}{5} = \frac{3}{5}.$$

4.5 Interpretation

LEARNING SUMMARY

After studying this section, you will be able to:

● **analyse and compare data presented in a variety of forms**

Comparing data

You need to be able to compare sets of data and draw conclusions about them. Here are some examples to illustrate the techniques.

Example

The children in a Year 7 class record the time it takes them to run between two marker posts.

The results are:

Time (seconds)								
Boys	46	47	49	61	43	54	48	52
	55	55	50	49	48	54	49	46
Girls	46	48	48	56	47	54	55	64
	49	51	47	52	49	49	65	63

Compare the distributions of the times for boys and girls.

Boys	mean = 50.38	**Girls**	mean = 52.69
	median = 49		median = 50
	mode = 49		mode = 49
	range = 18		range = 19

For both boys and girls the median, mode and range are similar but the mean for the girls is slightly higher so one could deduce that the girls are slightly slower than the boys.

You could show the distributions using a stem and leaf table.

Here the numbers for girls and boys have been put in order.

```
        Girls                          Boys
9  9   9   8   8   7   7   6 | 4 | 3   6   6   7   8   8   9   9   9
       6   5   4   2   1 | 5 | 0   2   4   4   5   5
               5   4   3 | 6 | 1
```

This is a 'back to back' stem and leaf table. The central column shows the 'tens' part of each number.

This gives an impression of the distribution of both sets of data and shows, for example, that more girls than boys took more than 60 seconds.

Example

Here are a list of English test results for two groups of students.

Group A	52	53	45	57	48	49	53	53	56	58	59	54	62	53
Group B	52	53	45	57	48	49	53	53	56	58	59			

Calculate the mean, median, mode and range for each set of data and compare the two groups' performance in English.

Group A   mean = 53.7, median = 53, mode = 53, range = 17
Group B   mean = 53, median = 53, mode = 53, range = 13

Comments could include: although the means are virtually the same, group B's is slightly lower than Group A's so one could argue that Group B is a little weaker in English but the range for Group B is smaller so the students in Group B are more consistent.

Example

A market gardener grows plum trees. He experiments with different fertilisers to see which fertiliser gives the best results. The table gives the weights, in grams, of the plums from 25 trees using each fertiliser.

Fertiliser A

79	91	48	86	44	67	54	36	83	55
79	26	82	68	77	80	18	42	61	76
24	20	56	73	69					

Fertiliser B

92	34	54	79	71	89	40	80	54	88
93	61	25	48	90	99	56	28	78	91
41	53	51	73	78					

Compare the two sets of data using the mean, median, mode and range. Which fertiliser do you think is best?

Fertiliser A: mean = 59.8, median = 67, mode = 79, range = 73
Fertiliser B: mean = 62.9, median = 71, mode = 54 and 78, range = 74
Note the results for fertiliser B are bi-modal.
Fertiliser B seems to give better results for it shows a higher mean and median.

PROGRESS CHECK

1 The temperatures of two towns were recorded for 12 days:

Day	1	2	3	4	5	6	7	8	9	10	11	12
Town A	11	13	12	11	14	15	17	15	16	15	20	18
Town B	10	12	15	13	16	12	15	16	14	16	17	21

Compare the temperatures for the two towns using mean, median, mode and range.

1 A: mean = 14.75, median = 15, mode = 15, range = 7
B: mean = 14.75; median = 15; mode = 16, range = 11
Town B has the higher mode, but the range of temperatures for town A is smaller so there is less variation.

Sample IGCSE questions

1   In a survey conducted in a shopping centre shoppers were asked the distances, in kilometres, from their homes to the centre. The results are shown in the table:

Distance, x km	$0 < x \leqslant 5$	$5 < x \leqslant 10$	$10 < x \leqslant 15$	$15 < x \leqslant 20$	$20 < x \leqslant 25$	$25 < x \leqslant 30$
Frequency	38	42	76	30	10	4

(a)   Write down the modal class.   **[2]**

(b)   Calculate an estimate for the mean distance.   **[5]**

Distance, x km	Cumulative frequency
$0 < x \leqslant 5$	38
$5 < x \leqslant 10$	
$10 < x \leqslant 15$	
$15 < x \leqslant 20$	
$20 < x \leqslant 25$	
$25 < x \leqslant 30$	

(c)   Complete the cumulative frequency table: **[3]**

(d)   Draw a cumulative frequency graph, using a scale of 2 cm for 5 km on the horizontal axis and 1 cm for 10 shoppers on the vertical axis.   **[4]**

(e)   Use your graph to estimate:

   (i)   the median distance   **[2]**

   (ii)   the interquartile range   **[3]**

(f)   What percentage of shoppers live more than 6 km away from the centre?   **[4]**

The modal class is the class with the highest frequency →

(a)   *The modal class is $10 < x \leqslant 15$.*   ✔✔

(b)   *Using the mid-points of each interval:*
$$(38 \times 2.5) + (42 \times 7.5) + (76 \times 12.5) + (30 \times 17.5)$$
$$+ (10 \times 22.5) + (4 \times 27.5)$$ ✔
$$= 95 + 315 + 950 + 525 + 225 + 110$$ ✔
$$= 2220$$ ✔
$$mean = 2220 \div 200$$ ✔
$$= 11.1 \ km$$ ✔

(c)

distance, x km	cumulative frequency
$0 < x \leqslant 5$	38
$5 < x \leqslant 10$	80
$10 < x \leqslant 15$	156
$15 < x \leqslant 20$	186
$20 < x \leqslant 25$	196
$25 < x \leqslant 30$	200

✔✔✔
(Lose 1 mark for each error)

Sample IGCSE questions

(d)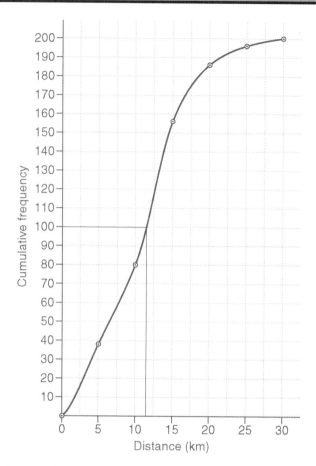

(1 mark for correct axes, scales and labels ✔✔✔✔
2 marks for correctly plotting points, but lose 1 mark for each mistake.
1 mark for a correct line drawn through the points.)

Plot the points at the end of each class interval, i.e. at 5, 10, 15, etc.

(e) (i) median distance = 11.5 km ✔✔
(this mark would be awarded on correctly interpreting your
graph, so draw line across the page at the median value to show
how you obtained your answer).

(ii) lower quartile = 6.75, upper quartile = 14.25, interquartile
range = 7.5 ✔✔✔

(f) number of shoppers ≤ 6 km = 44 ✔
number ≥ 6 km = 156 ✔

percentage = $\dfrac{156}{200} \times 100 = 78$ ✔✔

2 The letters of the word 'PROCESSES' are written on individual cards
and placed in a bag.

| P | R | O | C | E | S | S | E | S |

A letter is selected at random from the bag and then replaced.

(a) What is the probability that the letter is:

(i) E [1]

(ii) a vowel [1]

Sample IGCSE questions

(iii) T **[1]**

(iv) not S **[1]**

The experiment is repeated 300 times.

(b) How many times would you expect the letter S to be chosen?

[3]

> *This is an easy probability question included as revision.*

(a) (i) $\dfrac{2}{9}$ ✔

(ii) $\dfrac{3}{9} = \dfrac{1}{3}$ ✔

(iii) 0 ✔

(iv) $\dfrac{6}{9} = \dfrac{2}{3}$ ✔

(b) *Probability of choosing S =* $\dfrac{1}{3}$ ✔

> *Always simplify the fractions where possible*

number of times S is chosen in 300 trials = $\dfrac{1}{3} \times 300 = 100$ ✔✔

3 Julie is taking a French examination. It consists of three parts: a reading test, a writing test and a talking and listening test.

The probability of her passing the reading test is 0.6. The probability of her passing the writing test is 0.7. The probability of her passing the talking and listening test is 0.4.

(a) Complete the tree diagram showing the possible outcomes of the three tests taken in the order shown. **[5]**

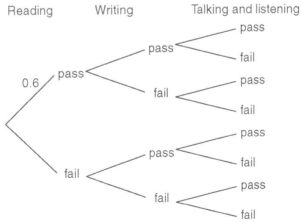

(b) What is the probability that she passes all three tests? **[3]**

(c) What is the probability that she passes at least two of the tests? **[4]**

(d) If Julie only passes one test she needs to repeat all three tests later in the year. What is the probability that Julie repeats all three tests? **[2]**

Sample IGCSE questions

(a)

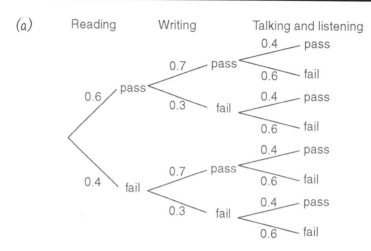

Reading   Writing   Talking and listening

(You will score 1 mark for completing the reading section, 2 marks for completing the writing section and 2 marks for completing the talking section.)

(b)   Multiplying along the branches:

$0.6 \times 0.7 \times 0.4$ ✔✔

$= 0.168$ ✔

(c)   The probabilities are added together giving:

$(PPP) + (PPF) + (PFP) + (FPP)$ ✔

$= 0.168 + 0.252 + 0.072 + 0.112$ ✔✔

$= 0.604$ ✔

(d)   1 subtract the answer to part (c) $= 1 - 0.604$ ✔

$= 0.396$ ✔

4   A dentist's patients are divided by age into groups as shown in the table below.

These questions usually involve independent and exclusive events. Make sure you know when to multiply and when to add.

Age, x years	Number of patients
$0 < x \leqslant 5$	14
$5 < x \leqslant 15$	41
$15 < x \leqslant 25$	59
$25 < x \leqslant 45$	70
$45 < x \leqslant 75$	16

(a)   Draw a histogram to show this distribution.   **[5]**

(b)   The dentist wishes to choose a stratified random sample of 40 patients.
Show how this can be done.   **[4]**

Sample IGCSE questions

Calculate the frequency densities.

(a)

Age, x (years)	Number of patients	Frequency density
$0 \leqslant x < 5$	14	2.8
$5 \leqslant x < 15$	41	4.1
$15 \leqslant x < 25$	59	5.9
$25 \leqslant x < 45$	70	3.5
$45 \leqslant x < 75$	16	0.5

✔✔✔

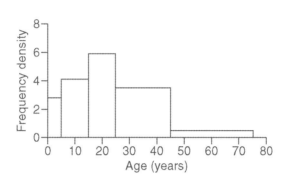

✔✔

(b)   The total number of patients = 14 + 41 + 59 + 70 + 16 = 200   ✔
the numbers required in each age group are therefore:

$$= \frac{14}{200} \times 40 = 2, \text{ i.e. } 3$$ ✔✔✔

$$\frac{41}{200} \times 40 = 8.2, \text{ i.e. } 8$$

$$\frac{59}{200} \times 40 = 11.8, \text{ i.e. } 12$$

$$\frac{70}{200} \times 40 = 14$$

Show your calculations so that you will earn method marks even if you make a mistake.

$$\frac{16}{200} \times 40 = 3.2, \text{ i.e. } 3$$

(3 marks for these calculations, lose 1 for each mistake)

Exam practice questions

1 The graph shows the quarterly sales, in $10 000s of plants and garden equipment at Shrubs'R'Us garden centre over a four-year period.

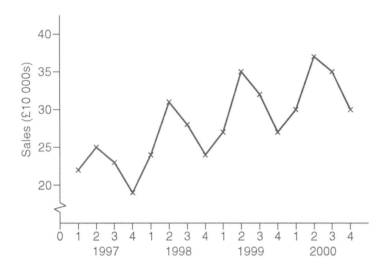

Year	Quarter	Sales $10 000's	Four-point moving average
1997	1	22	
	2	25	
	3	23	
	4	19	
1998	1	24	
	2	31	
	3	28	
	4	24	
1999	1	27	
	2	35	
	3	32	
	4	27	
2000	1	30	
	2	37	
	3	35	
	4	30	

(a) Copy the table and calculate the four-point moving averages for this data and enter the values on the table. **[3]**

(b) Plot these moving averages on the graph. **[2]**

(c) Draw the trend line. **[1]**

Exam practice questions

2 Martin's Bank have conducted a survey of people with savings accounts with the bank. The results are shown in the table:

Age, y (years)	Number of people	Cumulative frequency
$0 \leqslant y < 5$	0	
$5 \leqslant y < 15$	100	
$15 \leqslant y < 25$	500	
$25 \leqslant y < 35$	800	
$35 \leqslant y < 45$	1000	
$45 \leqslant y < 55$	1400	
$55 \leqslant y < 65$	2500	
$65 \leqslant y < 75$	900	

(a) Complete the cumulative frequency table. **[2]**
(b) Draw a cumulative frequency curve for this data. **[1]**
(c) Use your graph to estimate:
  (i) the interquartile range of the ages **[2]**
  (ii) the number of people over 62 years old who have savings accounts with the bank. **[2]**

3 The table gives the distances travelled to work each day by a group of 50 employees:

Distance, d (miles)	Frequency
$0 < d \leqslant 2.5$	16
$2.5 < d \leqslant 3.5$	9
$3.5 < d \leqslant 4.5$	11
$4.5 < d \leqslant 6.5$	10
$6.5 < d \leqslant 10.5$	4

(a) Fred claims that the median and mode of these distances are both equal to 4.6 miles. Which of these claims is incorrect and why? **[2]**
(b) Construct a histogram to display the data. **[3]**

4 (a) Jodi has 10 T-shirts. 7 are white and 3 are green.
    She chooses one at random.
    Naomi has 8 T-shirts. 1 is white, 2 are green and 5 are red.
    She chooses one at random.
    What is the probability that Jodi and Naomi choose the same coloured T-shirt? **[5]**

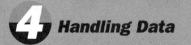

Exam practice questions

(b) Jen has 7 T-shirts. 2 are white, 4 are green and 1 is red. She chooses three at random. What is the probability that Jen chooses T-shirts that are all the same colour?

[3]

5 A hospital recorded the birth weights, in kilograms, of 100 boys and 100 girls. The weights are summarised in the table below.

	Minimum	Lower quartile	Median	Upper quartile	Maximum
Girls	1.5	2.5	3.2	3.8	4.6
Boys	1.3	2.3	3.4	4.1	4.9

(a) Draw two box plots for the weights of the boys and girls to show this data. **[3]**

(b) Compare the weights of the boys and the girls. **[2]**

6 A coin is biased. The probability that it lands showing heads is 0.7.
To play a game the coin is tossed three times.
Find the probability that more heads than tails are obtained. **[3]**

Unit 1

1 (a) $2 \times 3 \times 3 \times 5 \times 13$ or $2 \times 3^2 \times 5 \times 13$

(b) (i) $\frac{1}{2} \times 4 = 2$

(ii) $\frac{\sqrt{3}}{3\sqrt{3}} = \frac{1}{3}$

(c) $3 \times 10^{-2} + 8 \times 10^{-1} = 0.83 = 8.3 \times 10^{-1}$

In part (a) there are part marks for a correct method or some correct factors, e.g., if 13 was omitted but $2 \times 3^2 \times 5$ shown, then 2 marks would be given. Intermediate steps or their equivalents earn part marks in (b) and (c), as shown. Correct answers earn full marks but to omit the working risks scoring zero.

2 (a) (i) $1\frac{15}{100} = 1\frac{3}{20}$

(ii) If F is the value of the fraction, then,
$$100F = 115.1\dot{5}$$
$$F = 1.1\dot{5}$$
Subtracting, $99F = 114$
$$F = \frac{114}{99} = 1\frac{15}{99} = 1\frac{5}{33}$$

(b) (i) $1 + 2 \times 1 \times \sqrt{2} + (\sqrt{2})^2 = 3 + 2\sqrt{2}$
Irrational

(ii) $1 + \sqrt{2} - \sqrt{2} - (\sqrt{2})^2 = 1 - 2 = -1$
Rational

(iii) $\dfrac{1-\sqrt{2}}{(1-\sqrt{2})(1+\sqrt{2})}$
$$= \frac{1-\sqrt{2}}{-1} = \sqrt{2} - 1$$
Irrational

For recurring decimals, always multiply by the power of 10 that lines up the pattern. To demonstrate that a number is rational or irrational it is necessary to get the number in the form shown in these answers. In part (b)(iii) the surd is in the denominator and the trick is to multiply top and bottom by a number that makes the denominator rational. Notice that part (ii) helped to find this number.

3 (a) $7.99 \div 1.175 = 68$ ¢

(b) (i) $\dfrac{79.9}{69.9} \times 100 = 114.3$
14.3% increase

(ii) $79.9 \times (1.143)^5 = 155.9$ ¢

Don't be tempted to multiply by 0.825 in part (a) — this is a reverse percentage. A good check is to increase your answer by 17.5% to see if it goes back to 79.9. There is a mark in (b)(ii) for multiplying by any power of 1.143.

4 (a) Maximum distance $= 2.05 \times 92.5$
$$= 189.625 \text{ km}$$

(b) Least fuel rate $= \dfrac{22.5}{189.625}$
$$= 0.12 \text{ litres/km}$$

In each case there is a mark for choosing correctly the highest or lowest value. Don't forget to find the least value, divide by the greatest.

5 (a) $1\frac{2}{5} + 3\frac{3}{4} = 4 + \frac{2}{5} + \frac{3}{4}$
$$= 4 + \frac{8+15}{20} = 4\frac{23}{20} = 5\frac{3}{20}$$

(b) $1\frac{2}{5} \times 3\frac{3}{4} = \frac{7}{5} \times \frac{15}{4}$
$$= \frac{7}{1} \times \frac{3}{4} = \frac{21}{4} = 5\frac{1}{4}$$

(c) $3\frac{1}{3} - 2\frac{5}{6} = \frac{10}{3} - \frac{17}{6} = \frac{20-17}{6}$
$$= \frac{3}{6} = \frac{1}{2}$$

The solution to part (b) shows the common factor 5 cancelled but you could multiply out first to get $(\frac{105}{20})$ and then cancel. This is longer. There is a short way in part (c). $3\frac{1}{3}$ is $\frac{1}{3}$ more than 3 and $2\frac{5}{6}$ is $\frac{1}{6}$ less than 3. $\frac{1}{3} + \frac{1}{6} = \frac{1}{2}$.

6 (a) {1, 2, 4, 8, 16}

(b) {1, 2, 4, 8, 16, 32}

(c) {32}

(d) 6

(e) ϕ

7

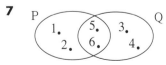

8 Since $(180 - x) + x + (135 - x) + 45 = 290$,
$x = 70$.
so, **70** families read both the papers.

Unit 2

1 (a) (i) $6 - 3x = 2x - 12$
$$18 = 5x$$
$$x = 3\tfrac{3}{5}$$

(ii) $3x - 2(x - 1) = 6$
$$x + 2 = 6$$
$$x = 4$$

(b) (i) $4x \leqslant 6x - 9$
$$9 \leqslant 2x$$
$$x \geqslant 4\tfrac{1}{2}$$

(ii) $x \leqslant 15$
$$x \leqslant -15$$
(or $-15 \leqslant x \geqslant 15$)

Take care with the direction of the inequality signs in part (b)(i). The method shown (keeping the x-term positive and reading the inequality backwards) avoids dividing by a negative number. However, this gives the same solution ($-2x \leqslant -9$, $x \geqslant 4$, changing the inequality sign on dividing by -2).

2 (a) $\dfrac{1}{v} = \dfrac{1}{u} - \dfrac{1}{f}$

$\dfrac{1}{v} = \dfrac{f - u}{uf}$

$v = \dfrac{uf}{f - u}$

(b) $p(r - q) = rq$
$pr - pq = rq$
$rq + pq = pr$
$q(r + p) = pr$
$q = \dfrac{pr}{r + p}$

In part (b), don't miss the fact that the new subject occurs twice in the formula and so you must first collect those terms.

3 x cents is the cost of a cup of coffee, y cents is the cost of a biscuit.

$2x + 3y = 323$ $\qquad$ $3x + y = 292$
$\qquad\qquad\qquad\qquad$ $2x + 3y = 323$
$\qquad\qquad\qquad\qquad$ $9x + 3y = 876$
$\qquad\qquad\qquad\qquad$ $-7x = -553$
$\qquad\qquad\qquad\qquad$ $x = 79¢$
$\qquad\qquad\qquad\qquad$ $y = 292 - 3 \times 79 = 55¢$

Choose your own letters for the variables. If you do not use an algebraic method to find the solution, you will lose most of the marks.

4 (a)

x	-1	-0.5	0	0.5	1	1.5	2	3
y	-2	0.375	1	0.625	0	-0.125	1	10

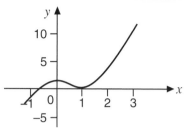

Draw a smooth curve through the points plotted.

(b) (i) $x = -0.6, 1, 1.6$
(ii) $x = 2.6$

(c) $x = 2.6$ $\qquad$ $f(x) = 0.056$
$x = 2.55$ $\qquad$ $f(x) = -0.423\ldots$
$x = 2.59$ $\qquad$ $f(x) = -0.042\ldots$
$x = 2.595$ $\quad$ $f(x) = -0.0067\ldots$
Solution $x = 2.59$

The solutions in part (b)(i) should be those from your graph. If you have made a mistake in drawing the graph, these marks could be earned so long as the readings were taken at the appropriate y values. To obtain full marks in part (c), you should show that the solution is nearer 2.59 than 2.6.

5 $y = 3 - 2x$
$y^2 = 9 - 12x + 4x^2$
$x^2 + 9 - 12x + 4x^2 = 16$
$5x^2 - 12x - 7 = 0$
$x = \dfrac{12 \pm \sqrt{12^2 + 4 \times 5 \times 7}}{2 \times 5}$
$x = 2.89$ or -0.49
$y = -2.77$ or 3.97
Points are $(2.89, -2.77)$, $(-0.49, 3.97)$

6 (a) $(x - 5)(x + 3)$
(b) $x = 5$ or $-x = -3$
(c) Either $x - 5$ and $x + 5 > 0$ so $x > 5$
or $x - 5 < 0$ and $x + 5 < 0$ so $x < -3$

In part (c), the brackets must both have the same sign, i.e., both negative or both positive, if the product is to be positive. This gives pairs of inequalities, both of which must be satisfied. However, only one counts, for example, if $x > 5$ then it is certainly $x > -3$ but there are values for which $x > -3$ but not > 5, so $x. > 5$ is the required condition. Similarly for the other pair.

7 (a) (b)

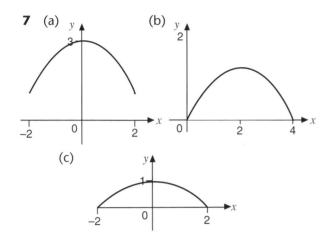

(c)

To check your work, test to see if known points fit. For example, in part (b), when $x = 2$, $y = f(0)$. From the original sketch of the function, $f(0) = 2$. Your sketch should have gone through (2, 2).

Unit 3

1 (a) (i) 105° (corresponding angles) [1]
(ii) 25° (= 180 − 50° − 105°,
angle on a straight line) [1]
(iii) 25° (alternate angles) [1]
(iv) 130° (angles in an isosceles triangle) [2]

(b) Angles PQX and SXR are equal
(corresponding angles)
Angles QXP and XRS are equal
(corresponding angles)
QX = XR (given) [1]
Therefore triangles are congruent
(ASA) [1]

In part (b) the question says 'prove' so explanations and reasons are required.

2 (b) Could be volume because it is the only formula with just one term involving r^3.
The $\dfrac{\pi r^2}{4}$ in the answer to part (c) means

that this answer represents something which is not just volume.

3 Cos AON $= \dfrac{8}{17}$

∴ angle AON = 61.9° [1]

Area of sector OAX $\text{OAX} = \dfrac{61.9}{360} \times \pi \times 17^2$

$= 156 \text{ cm}^2$ [1]

AN $= \sqrt{17^2 - 8^2} = 15$ [1]

Area of triangle AON $= \dfrac{1}{2} \times 8 \times 15 = 60 \text{ cm}^2$ [1]
∴ shaded area =
156 − 60 = 96 cm² [1]

Follow through marks would be available in this multi-step problem. This means that if you made a mistake in your calculation in an early part of the solution as long as you used your wrong answer correctly later on no further loss of marks would arise.

4 (a) $\overrightarrow{XN} = \dfrac{1}{2}\overrightarrow{XY}$ and $\overrightarrow{XY} = \overrightarrow{OB} = \mathbf{b}$

∴ $\overrightarrow{XN} = \dfrac{1}{2}\mathbf{b}$ [1]

$\overrightarrow{ON} = \overrightarrow{OX} + \overrightarrow{XN} = \dfrac{1}{2}\mathbf{a} + \dfrac{1}{2}\mathbf{b}$ [1]

$\overrightarrow{AN} = \overrightarrow{AX} + \overrightarrow{XN} = -\dfrac{1}{2}\mathbf{a} + \dfrac{1}{2}\mathbf{b} = \dfrac{1}{2}\mathbf{b} - \dfrac{1}{2}\mathbf{a}$ [1]

$\overrightarrow{NB} = \overrightarrow{NY} + \overrightarrow{YB} = \dfrac{1}{2}\mathbf{b} - \dfrac{1}{2}\mathbf{a}$ [1]

(b) $\overrightarrow{AB} = \overrightarrow{AC} + \overrightarrow{CB} = \mathbf{b} - \mathbf{a}$ [1]

$\overrightarrow{AN} = \dfrac{1}{2}(\mathbf{b} - \mathbf{a})$

$\overrightarrow{AB} = \dfrac{1}{2}(\mathbf{b} - \mathbf{a})$

∴ A, N, B all lie on the same straight line, with N as mid-point. [1]

Take care over the directions and hence the signs of the vectors.

5 (a) AC² = 100² + 65² [1]
AC = 119.27 km [1]
= 119 km (to 3 s.f.) [1]

(b) tan BCA $= \dfrac{100}{65}$ [1]

Angle BCA = 56.98° ie 57° [1]
Bearing = 180° + 3°
= 183° [2]

(c) Speed $= \left(\dfrac{100 \text{ km}}{18 \text{ min}}\right) = \dfrac{100 \times 60}{18}$ [2]

$= 333 \text{ km/h (to 3 s.f.)}$ [2]

In part (b) draw a 'north-south' line at C as follows:

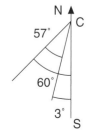

6 (a) Curved surface area $= \pi rl$

$$l = l = \sqrt{8^2 + 6^2}$$
$$= 10 \text{ cm} \qquad [1]$$

Curved surface area $= \pi \times 6 \times 10$
$$= 60\pi \text{ cm}^2 \qquad [2]$$

(b) $V = \frac{1}{3}\pi r^2 h$

$$= \frac{1}{3} \times \pi \times 36 \times 8 \qquad [1]$$

$$= 96\pi \text{ cm}^3 \qquad [1]$$

(c) Area of sector $= \dfrac{x}{360} \times \pi r^2 \qquad [1]$

$$\therefore \quad \frac{x}{360} \times \pi 10^2 = 60\pi \qquad [1]$$

$$\therefore \quad x = \frac{60 \times 360}{100} = 216° \qquad [1]$$

As with question 3 there would be follow through marks available here. Remember to show all your working through the intermediate steps. Remember too that the radius of the sector is the slant height of the cone. (Make a cone from a sector of a circle like this if you are not sure.)

7 (a)

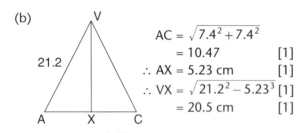

Angle AVD $= 2 \times \sin\left(\dfrac{3.7}{21.2}\right) \qquad [2]$
$$= 2 \times 10.05 \qquad [1]$$
$$= 20.1° \qquad [1]$$

(b)

AC $= \sqrt{7.4^2 + 7.4^2}$
$$= 10.47 \qquad [1]$$
$\therefore$ AX $= 5.23$ cm $\qquad [1]$
$\therefore$ VX $= \sqrt{21.2^2 - 5.23^3} \qquad [1]$
$$= 20.5 \text{ cm} \qquad [1]$$

(c) $\cos$ VAX $= \dfrac{5.23}{21.2} \qquad [2]$

$\therefore$ angle VAX $= 75.7° \qquad [1]$

Draw sketches, as shown above, to help you identify sides and angles. Again follow through marks would be available - but remember to show all your working.

8 (a) This is a standard drawing, see page 116 [2]
(b) $(90°, 0)$, $(270°, 0)$ [2]
(c) $\cos x = 0.8$ [1]
(d) If $\cos x = 0.8$ there are 2 solutions so the angle could be in the first or the fourth quadrant — see page 115
Solving $x = \cos^{-1} 0.8$ on a calculator gives x

$$= 36.87° \text{ i.e. } 36.9° \qquad [1]$$
$\therefore$ the other angle $= 360° - 36.9° = 323.1° \qquad [1]$

Draw a sketch to help you decide where the second solution lies:

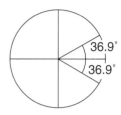

Unit 4

1 (a) Averages are:
(in $10 000s) 22.25, 22.75, 24.25, 25.5, 26.75, 27.5, 28.5, 29.5, 30.25, 31, 31.5, 32.25, 33

(b) Check your graph, plotting the values given in part (a). [2]

(c) You should be able to draw a straight line passing through virtually every point. [1]

Remember to plot the moving averages between the quarterly values given. On the graph the first average is plotted at the point (2.5, 22.25), the next at (3.5, 22.75) and so on.

2 (a) Cumulative frequencies are 0, 100, 600, 1400, 2400, 3800, 6300, 7200

(b) You can check the accuracy of your curve by looking at the given answers for part (c).

(c) (i) UQ $= 61$, LQ $= 39$, IQR $= 22$ [1 + 1]
(ii) 1600 to 1700 [1]

In part (c) remember to find the median first and then to find the LQ and the UQ. An easy way of doing this is to treat the lower quartile as the median of the values below the actual median and the upper quartile as the median of the values in the upper half, i.e. above the actual median.

3 (a) Median cannot be 4.6 because 36 distances are less than this.

(b) Frequency densities are 5, 10, 14, 4.5, 1.75.

For part (b) you are not given the scales to use so you must choose sensible scales for both axes, for example use 2 cm for 2 miles on the horizontal axis and 2 cm for 5 units on the frequency density, (the vertical) axis.

4 (a) Probability that Jodi chooses white $= \dfrac{7}{10}$ [1]

and that she chooses green = $\frac{3}{10}$

Probability that Naomi chooses white = $\frac{1}{8}$ [1]

and that she chooses green = $\frac{2}{8}$

Therefore the probability that both choose

white $= \frac{7}{10} \times \frac{1}{8} = \frac{7}{80}$ [1]

probability that both choose

green $= \frac{3}{10} \times \frac{2}{8} = \frac{6}{80}$ [1]

Therefore the probability that both choose the same

$= P(W,W) + P(G,G) = \frac{7}{80} + \frac{6}{80} = \frac{13}{80}$ [1]

(b) To pick 3 of the same colour Jen must pick green. [1]

First 'pick' the probability = $\frac{4}{7}$; for the

second the probability = $\frac{3}{6}$,

and, for the third, the probability = $\frac{2}{5}$ [1]

∴ the probability = $\frac{4}{7} \times \frac{3}{6} \times \frac{2}{5} = \frac{4}{35}$ [1]

Remember (i)   when to add probabilities
(ii)   when to multiply
(iii) that the sum of probabilities is 1

5 (a) Check your drawings using the values given in the table. There would be 1 mark for the girls' box plot correct, 1 mark for the boys' and 1 mark for using suitable scales [3]

(b) Boys' average weight is greater than girls'. Boys' weights are more spread out, therefore more varied. The interquartile range, i.e. the middle 50% is wider than for the girls.
[1 mark for any valid observation up to a maximum of 2]

Remember to comment about the position of the median leading to a comment about spread and distribution and try to compare rather than comment on only the boys or the girls.

6

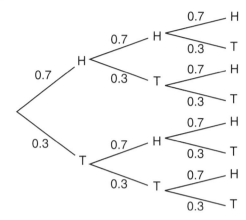

Probability of
HHH = 0.7 × 0.7 × 0.7   = 0.343
HHT = 0.7 × 0.7 × 0.3   = 0.147
HTH = 0.7 × 0.3 × 0.7   = 0.147
THH = 0.3 × 0.7 × 0.7   = 0.147
total   = 0.784

[1 mark awarded for multiplying probabilities, 1 mark for adding the separate totals and 1 mark for the final answer].

A probability tree diagram, which may be given in the question (although you would have to complete by marking on the probabilities) is a logical method to use in questions like this because it shows all the possibilities.

Model Test Paper

Based on the IGCSE Paper 2 (Extended)

Time: 1 hour 30 minutes   **Total Marks:** 70

Useful Formulae

Volume of prism = (area of cross section) × length

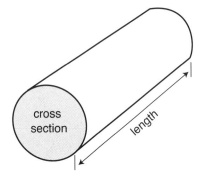

In any triangle *ABC*,

Sine rule: $\dfrac{a}{\sin A} = \dfrac{b}{\sin B} = \dfrac{c}{\sin C}$

Cosine rule: $a^2 = b^2 + c^2 - 2bc \cos A$

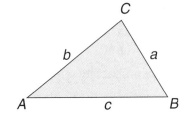

Area of triangle = $\dfrac{1}{2} ab \sin C$

Volume of sphere = $\dfrac{4}{3} \pi r^3$

Surface area of sphere = $4\pi r^2$

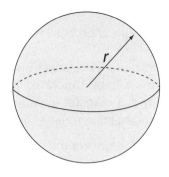

Volume of cone = $\dfrac{1}{3} \pi r^2 h$

Curved area of cone = $\pi r l$

The quadratic equation

The solutions of $ax^2 + bx + c = 0$, where $a \neq 0$, are given by $x = \dfrac{-b \pm \sqrt{(b^2 - 4ac)}}{2a}$

1 A train left Delhi a 1930 hours on Wednesday, March 8th and arrived in Mumbai the following day at 1435 hours. How long, in hours and minutes, was the journey?

Answers: .... hr. .... min. **[2]**

2 Which of the following numbers are irrational? Write them is ascending order:

$$\frac{3}{4} \quad \pi \quad \sqrt{4} \quad \frac{1}{\sqrt{9}} \quad 0 \quad \sqrt{8} \quad \sqrt[3]{8}$$

Answer: .... **[2]**

3 The number who attended a cricket match was 18,540, correct to the nearest 10. Complete the statement about the limits of P:

Answer: .... $\leq P <$ .... **[2]**

4 Use your calculator to find the value of (a) 8 tan 42° (b) 7 cos 31°. (to 3 significant figures)

Answer: (a) .... **[1]**

Answer: (b) .... **[1]**

5 Simplify $\frac{3}{4}q^9 \div \frac{1}{2}q^{-6}$.

Answer: .... **[2]**

6 Solve the equation: $\frac{2x}{7} - 5 = 3$.

Answer: .... **[2]**

7 Work out $1\frac{1}{2}\left(2\frac{3}{4} + 1\frac{1}{3}\right) \div \left(8\frac{5}{8} - 2\frac{1}{2}\right)$.

Answer: .... **[3]**

8 Lydia puts \$4,000 in a bank where it earns compound interest at the rate of 5% per year. Calculate the interest she will receive in the second year.

Answer: .... **[2]**

9 The population of the Earth will soon exceed 10 billion people. Write this number in standard form:

Answer: .... **[2]**

10 Solve the simultaneous equations

$$\frac{3}{4}x + y = 11$$
$$2x - 5y = -9.$$

Answer: .... **[2]**

11 Make p the subject of the formula:

$$3b = ap^2 - 2c.$$

Answer: .... **[2]**

12 For the shape shown, write down:

(a) the number of lines of symmetry   *Answer:* .... **[1]**

(b) the order of rotational symmetry   *Answer:* .... **[1]**

13 Mark's instructions to Raymond are: "Meet me at the signpost which is 6 km from the white rock, and is equidistant from the stone tower and the willow tree."

Using a scale of 1 cm: 2 km, use a compass and ruler to locate the signpost, and state how far the signpost is from Raymond's house. **[3]**

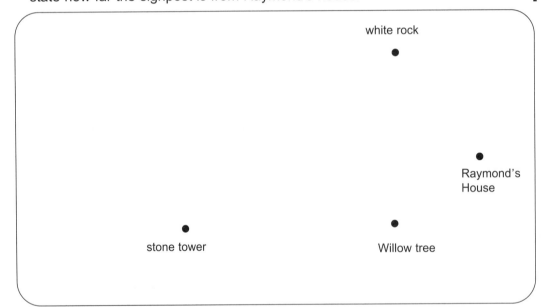

14 The area of triangle PQR is 108 cm² and the area of triangle PST is 12 cm². ST is parallel to QR and the length of ST is 6 cm. Calculate the length of QR.

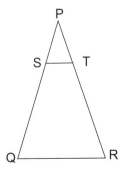

Answer: .... **[3]**

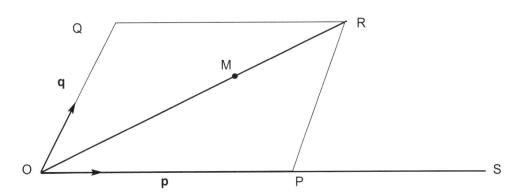

OPQR is a parallelogram. OP = **p**, OQ = **q**. M is a point such that OM: OR = 2:1.
S is a point such that P is the mid-point of OS.

Find, in terms of **p** and **q**

(a) $\overrightarrow{OR}$ *Answer:* .... **[2]**

(b) $\overrightarrow{QS}$ *Answer:* .... **[2]**

(c) $\overrightarrow{RM}$ *Answer:* .... **[2]**

(d) $\overrightarrow{RS}$ *Answer:* .... **[2]**

---

16 Dallas is 75 km due East of Forth Worth, and 58 km due North of Arlington. Find:

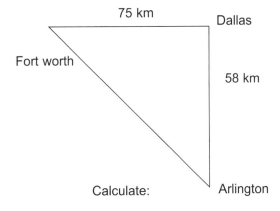

Not to Scale

Calculate:

(a) the distance between Fort Worth and Arlington

Answer: .... **[3]**

(b) the bearing of Fort Worth from Arlington, correct to the nearest degree.

Answer: .... **[3]**

---

17 $f(x) = \frac{1}{2}(3x - 2)$ and $g(x) = 2x + 5$.

Find the value of gf(2). *Answer:* .... **[2]**

Find the value of fg (−2). *Answer:* .... **[2]**

Solve the equation $g^{-1}(x) = -2$. *Answer:* .... **[2]**

---

18 (a) Factorise completely: $48p^2 - 27q^2$.

Answer: .... **[2]**

(b) Expand: $(2p - 5q)^2$.

Answer: .... **[2]**

(c) $x^2 - 8x + 15$ is to be written in the form $(x - p)^2 + q$.

Find the values of p and q.

Answer: .... **[2]**

---

19 $A = (4, -2), \; B = \begin{pmatrix} 1 & 7 \\ 2 & -3 \end{pmatrix}, \; C = \begin{pmatrix} 3 & 7 \\ 2 & -1 \end{pmatrix}, \; D = \begin{pmatrix} 6 \\ -5 \end{pmatrix}$

(a) Which **two** of the following matrix calculations are **not** possible?

(i) AB   **(ii) A − D**   **(iii) CB**   **(iv) AD**   **(v) CA**   **(vi) BD**

Answer: .... and .... **[2]**

(b) Calculate **BC**.

Answer: .... **[2]**

(c) Use your answer to part (b) to write down C^{-1}, the inverse of C.

Answer: .... **[2]**

---

20 The table shows the number of people dwelling in the houses of a particular street:

Number of people:	0	1	2	3	4	5	6	7
Frequency:	3	8	12	14	17	11	4	p

If the median of this data is 3, what is the maximum possible value of *p*?

Answer: .... **[2]**

21 The following graph is that of an athlete's race:

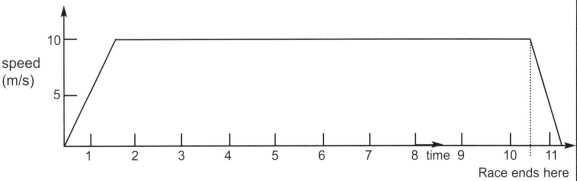

(a) Calculate his acceleration during the first second.

Answer: .... **[1]**

(b) What is the total distance covered in the race?

Answer: .... **[2]**

---

22. If *p* horses eat *q* bales of hay in t minutes, and assuming that all horses eat at the same constant rate, how many bales of hay are consumed by q horses in p minutes?

Answer: .... **[2]**

Model Test Paper

Based on the IGCSE Paper 4 (Extended)

Time: 2 hours 30 minutes   **Total Marks**: 130

1   Anita and Rita buy a television each.

(a)   Anita buys a size A set which has a price of $480. She pays 30% of this price and thereafter pays $30 per month for a year.

   (i)   How much does Anita pay in total?   **[2]**

   (ii)   What percentage increase does your answer to part (i) above, represent of the original price of $480?   **[2]**

(b)   Rita pays $459 for a size B set after a reduction of 15% in the price, in a sale. Calculate the original price of the size B set.   **[2]**

(c)   The picture size of a TV is quoted as the length of its diagonal. Anita's set size is 40 cm, as shown in the diagram:

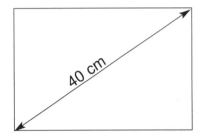

The ratio of Anita's and Rita's TV picture sizes are in the same ratio as their original prices.

Calculate the picture size of Rita's TV.   **[2]**

(d)   Anita and Rita watch TV for a total of 6 hrs. and 40 minutes on a weekend. The ratio of times for which Rita and Anita view television respectively = 3 : 5.

Calculate the time for which Rita watches TV.   **[2]**

(e)   The time of 6 hrs. and 40 minutes is only 25/32 of the total time for which the TV was viewed in the whole week. Calculate this total time.   **[2]**

(f)   The length of Anita's TV picture size is 32 cm. Calculate its width.   **[2]**

2.   **Answer all of this question on a sheet of graph paper.**

(a) $f(x) = x^2 - 2x - 6$

x	−3	−2	−1	0	1	2	3	4
$f(x)$	p	2	−3	−6	−7	q	−3	2

(i) Find the values of p and q. **[2]**

(ii) Draw the graph of $y = f(x)$ for $-3 \leqslant x \leqslant 4$.
Use a scale of 1 cm to represent one unit on each axis. **[4]**

(iii) By drawing a suitable line, estimate the gradient of the graph where $x = -1$. **[3]**

(b) $g(x) = 4 - \dfrac{|x|^3}{2}$

x	-3	-2	-1	0	1	2	3
$g(x)$	$-9\frac{1}{2}$	0	u	4	$3\frac{1}{2}$	v	$-9\frac{1}{2}$

(i) Find the values of u and v. **[2]**

(ii) On the same grid as part **(a–ii)**, draw the graph of $y = g(x)$ for $-3 \leqslant x \leqslant 3$. **[4]**

(c) Show that the equation $f(x) = g(x)$ simplifies to: $x^3 + 2x^2 - 4x - 20 = 0$. **[2]**

Use your graph to write down two solutions to the equation $x^3 + 2x^2 - 4x - 20 = 0$, giving both answers correct to one decimal place. **[4]**

3 The number of goals in each game scored by Newtown Rovers, a football team that plays in a league where each team plays every other team twice in the season – once at home and once away, is summarised in the frequency table below:

goals scored	0	1	2	3	4	5
frequency	7	11	p	4	2	1

(a) If the total number of goals scored by Newtown Rovers is 58, find the value of p. **[2]**

(b) If any one game is chosen at random when looking through the records for the season, what is the probability that Newtown Rovers scored four goals in it? **[2]**

(c) What is the average number of goals scored by Newtown Rovers for the season? **[2]**

(d) If the information in the frequency table is represented on a pie chart, how large would be sector, that represents the number of games in which Newtown Rovers scored three goals? **[2]**

(e) The league positions are determined by the number of points scored. Three points are awarded for a win, one for a draw and none for a loss. The goal difference, equal to the number of goals scored by a team minus the number of goals scored against it, is also recorded. Newtown Rovers finished third in the league; the top three places are as shown in the table:

(**Key:** P = games played, W = won, D = drew, L = lost, F = goals for, A = goals against, Diff = goal difference, Pts. = total points)

Team	P	W	D	L	F	A	Diff	Pts.
Power Rangers	36	20	11	5	89	32	57	71
Players United	36	18	12	6	77	25	52	66
Newtown Rovers	36	a	b	11	c	d	29	63

(i) Form two equations for a and b (one based on games played and the other on points won) and solve them simultaneously to find a and b. **[4]**

(ii) What are the values of c and d when the total number of goals scored are 59? **[2]**

4

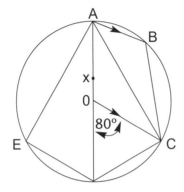

A circle, centred at O, passes through the points A, B, C, D, E. AD is a diameter of the circle, $C\hat{O}D = 80°$ and AB ∥ OC.

(a) Find   (i) $D\hat{A}C$ **[2]**

                (ii) $A\hat{D}C$ **[2]**

                (iii) $A\hat{B}C$ **[2]**

                (iv) $A\hat{C}B$ **[2]**

(b) X is the point on AD such that AX = 2/5 AD. Given that the area of triangle EAD is 80 cm², calculate the area of triangle EXD. **[2]**

(c) Given that the diameter of the circle is 16 cm, find the length of DC to 3 significant figures. **[4]**

5   Nelson walks a distance of 20 km from his home to a lighthouse, at an average speed of p km/hr.

(a) Write down, in terms of p, time taken in hours. **[1]**

He returns homewards from the lighthouse but this time he walks more quickly, at an average speed of ($p + 1$) kilometers per hour. The journey therefore takes less time – in fact, it takes just one hour less.

(b) Write down an equation in p and show that it simplifies to $p^2 + p - 20 = 0$. **[4]**

(c) Solve the equation $p^2 + p - 20 = 0$. **[2]**

(d) Find the time it takes for Nelson to walk to the lighthouse. **[2]**

6 Tennis balls are sold in threes in thin, sealed cylindrical containers. The diameter of a tennis ball is 7 cm, the diameter of the container is 8 cm and its height is 22 cm.

(a) What is the volume of air contained within a sealed container? **[5]**

For the wholesale market, cylinders are sold in boxes (cuboids) of thirty six. The cylinders are packed upright in a 6 × 6 arrangement, so that the length and width of the box are the same.

(b) What is the minimum length and height of a box? **[3]**

(c) What percentage of the total internal space of each box is occupied by the cylinders? **[5]**

7 (a) In a school of 800 students, 540 play volleyball and 490 play tennis while 170 play neither.

　　(i) By using a Venn diagram, or otherwise, find the number of students who play both the sports. **[3]**

　　(ii) If a student is chosen at random, what is the probability that he or she plays only tennis? **[1]**

　　(iii) If a student is chosen at random, what is the probability that he or she does not play volleyball? **[2]**

(b) Class A has 12 girls and 16 boys and class B has 18 girls and 10 boys.

　　(i) If a student is chosen at random from class A, what is the probability that she is a girl? **[1]**

　　(ii) If a student is chosen at random from class A and another one is chosen from class B, what is the probability that both are boys? **[2]**

　　(iii) A student is chosen at random from class A and another one is chosen from class B. What is the probability that one student is a girl and the other is a boy? **[3]**

8 A shop stocks x packets of Extra-juice which costs $1.50 per pack, and packets of Supper-juice, which costs $2.40 per pack.

(a) The shop allocates a maximum of $120 to stock both types of juice. Show that $5x + 8y \leqslant 400$. **[2]**

(b) The shop must stock at least 10 packets of Extra-juice and 15 packets of Super-juice.
Write down two inequalities to represent this information. **[2]**

(c) The number of packets of Super-juice in stock must not exceed the number of packets of Extra-juice.
Write down an inequality, in terms of x and y, to show this information. **[2]**

(d) Using a scale of 1 cm to represent 5 units on each axis, draw an *x*-axis for
$0 \leqslant x \leqslant 80$ and a *y*-axis for $0 \leqslant y \leqslant 90$. **[2]**

(e) Draw four lines on your graph to represent the inequalities you have written down, and
shade the **unwanted** regions. **[4]**

(f) When 40 packets of Extra-juice are held in stock, what is the maximum number of
Super-juice packets that can be stocked? **[1]**

(g) The profit on each Extra-juice is 35 cents and the profit on each Super-juice is 65
cents. Find the maximum profit possible. **[3]**

9

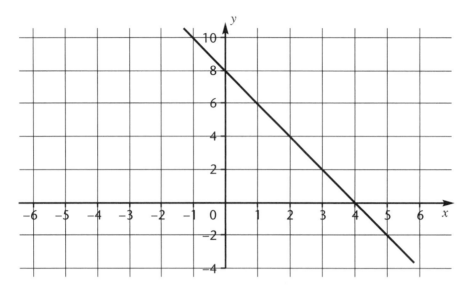

A straight line has been drawn on the grid

(a) Write down the equation of the straight line. **[2]**

(b) Write down the gradient of the line $x + 3y = 6$. **[2]**

(c) Write down the equation of the line which is parallel to the line with the equation
$4x + 2y = 8$ and passes through the point with coordinates $(0, -1)$. **[2]**

(d) Write down the equation of a line which is perpendicular to the line $y = 3x$. **[2]**

10 In the diagram $\overrightarrow{OD} = \mathbf{d}$, $\overrightarrow{OC} = \mathbf{2c}$ and $\overrightarrow{OE} = \mathbf{3d}$

F is the midpoint of CD and CG = $\dfrac{1}{4}$ CE.

(a) Express in terms of **c** and **d**.

　(i) $\overrightarrow{DC}$ **[1]**

　(ii) $\overrightarrow{DF}$ **[1]**

(b) Prove that O, F and G lie on a straight line. **[5]**

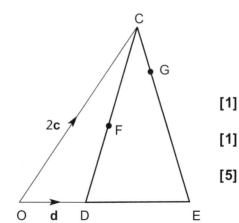

Model Test Answers: Paper 2

Question	Answer
1	19 hrs. 5 mins.
2	$\sqrt{8}, \pi$
3	$18,535 \leqslant P < 18,544$
4	1.20
5	$\frac{3}{2}q^{15}$
6	$x = 28$
7	1
8	\$210
9	1.0×10^{10}
10	$x = 8, y = 5$
11	$P = \sqrt{\frac{3b + 2c}{a}}$
12	**(a)** Lines of symmetry = 4
	(b) Order rotational symmetry = 4
13	Distance from Raymond's Home = 13 km.
14	QR = 18 cm
15	**(a)** $\overrightarrow{OR} = \boldsymbol{p} + \boldsymbol{q}$ **(b)** $\overrightarrow{QS} = 2\boldsymbol{p} + \boldsymbol{q}$
	(c) $\overrightarrow{RM} = \frac{1}{3}(\boldsymbol{q} - \boldsymbol{p})$ **(d)** $\overrightarrow{RS} = (\boldsymbol{p} - \boldsymbol{q})$
16	**(a)** 95 km **(b)** 308°
17	**(a)** $gf(2) = 9$; $fg(-2) = \frac{1}{2}$; $x = 1$
18	**(a)** $3(4p - 3q)(4p + 3q)$
	(b) $4p^2 - 20pq + 25g^3$
	(c) $p = 4, q = -1$
19	**(a)** $A - D$ and CA
	(b) $BC = \begin{pmatrix} 17 & 0 \\ 0 & 17 \end{pmatrix}$
	(c) $\frac{1}{17}\begin{pmatrix} 1 & 7 \\ 2 & -3 \end{pmatrix}$
20	Maximum value of $p = 4$
21	**(a)** Acceleration = 10 ms^{-2}.
	(b) Distance of race = 100 m.
22	$\frac{q^2}{t}$ bales of hay.

Model Test Answers: Paper 4

Question	Answer		Question	Answer

1 **(a) (i)** $504, **(ii)** 5%

(b) $540

(c) Rita's T.V. is 45 cm.

(d) Rita watches T.V. for 2 hours and 30 minutes.

(e) 8 hrs. 32 min.

(f) Width = 24 cm.

2 **(a) (i)** $p = 9, q = -6$

(ii)

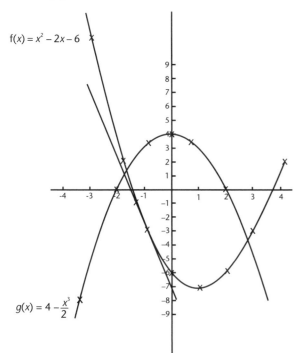

f(x) = $x^2 - 2x - 6$

g(x) = $4 - \dfrac{x^3}{2}$

(iii) See tangent to the graph, of slope $= -4$

(b) (i) $u = 3\frac{1}{2}, v = 0$

(ii) Refer to graph given in (a−ii)

$$x^2 - 2x - 6 = 4 - \frac{x^3}{2} \Rightarrow 2x^2 - 4x - 12 = 8 - x^3,$$

or $x^3 + 2x^2 - 4x - 20 = 0$.

(c) $x = -1.7$ or 2.7.

3 **(a)** $p = 11$; **(b)** $\dfrac{2}{36} = \dfrac{1}{18}$; **(c)** median = 1.5 goals

(d) 40°;

(e) (i) $a + b = 25$; $3a + b = 63 \Rightarrow a = 19$ and $b = 6$
(ii) c = 44 and d = 73

4 **(a)** $\hat{DAC} = 40°$

$\hat{ADC} = 50°$

$\hat{ABC} = 130°$

$\hat{ACB} = 10°$

(b) 48 cm^2

(c) 10.3 cm

5 **(a)** $\dfrac{20}{p}$

(b) $\dfrac{20}{p} = \dfrac{20}{p+1} + 1 \Rightarrow 20(p+1) = 20p + (p)(p+1)$

$\therefore \quad 20 = p^2 + p \Rightarrow p^2 + p - 20 = 0$

(c) $p = -5$ or $p = 4$. Here $p = -5$ is not a feasible solution. Hence, the speed is 4 km/hr.

(d) Nelson takes 5 hours to walk to the lighthouse.

6 **(a)** 14 cm^3

(b) length = 48 cm, width = 48 cm, height = 22 cm

(e) 78.6%

7 **(a)**

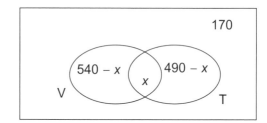

(i) 400

(ii) 9/80

(iii) 13/40

(b) (i) $\dfrac{3}{7}$ **(ii)** $\dfrac{10}{49}$ **(iii)** $\dfrac{51}{98}$

8 **(a)** $1.50x + 2.40y \leqslant 120$

$\Rightarrow 15x + 24y \leqslant 1200$

$\Rightarrow 5x + 8y \leqslant 400$

(b) $x \geqslant 10, y \geqslant 15$

(c) $y \leqslant x$

(d), (e) See graph

(f) 25 packets of Super-juice.

(g) 30 packets of Extra juice + 31 packets of Super juice give a profit of $30.65.

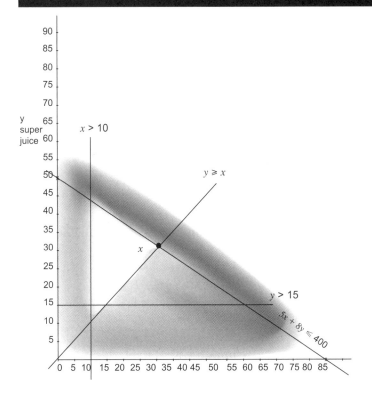

Lines $y = x$ and $5x + 8y = 400$ have a point of intersection at $x = 30.8$ and $y = 30.8$.

9 (a) $y = -2x + 8$

   (b) $-\dfrac{1}{3}$

   (c) $y = -2x - 1$

   (d) $y = -\dfrac{1}{3}x +$ any constant

10 (a) (i) $\overrightarrow{DC} = -\mathbf{d} + 2\mathbf{c}$

         (ii) $\overrightarrow{DF} = -\dfrac{1}{2}(-\mathbf{d} + 2\mathbf{c})$

    (b) $\overrightarrow{OF} = -\dfrac{1}{2}(\mathbf{d} + 2\mathbf{c})$

         $\overrightarrow{OG} = -\dfrac{3}{4}(\mathbf{d} + 2\mathbf{c})$

Since $\overrightarrow{OG}$ is a multiple of $\overrightarrow{OF}$, i.e., $\overrightarrow{OG} = \dfrac{3}{2}\overrightarrow{OF}$ and they go through the common point O; O, G and F must lie on a straight line.

Index